TREASURY
IN THE
MUNICH RESIDENCE

OFFICIAL GUIDE

1998

Bayerische Verwaltung der staatlichen Schlösser,
Gärten und Seen, München

Published by the Museum Department of the Bavarian Administration of the State Palaces, Gardens and Lakes. This seventh English edition of the Official Guide is an identical reprint of the sixth enlarged English edition, which was based on the third edition of the Catalogue of the Treasury of the Munich Residence, edited by Herbert Brunner, Munich 1970 (out of print). This English edition corresponds largely to the German edition of 1992, both of which were reviewed and supplemented by Sabine Heym, who also extended the illustrations.

Photographs: colour plates 9, 25, 32, Claus Hansmann, Stockdorf near Munich; all others, Bayerische Verwaltung der staatlichen Schlösser, Gärten und Seen, Munich.

Translated by Ingrid Taylor

Cover: Cat. 643 Pendant (known as the "Palatine Lion") German, c. 1570 – 1580

7th English edition, 76th – 83th thousand

© 1998 Bayerische Verwaltung der staatlichen Schlösser, Gärten und Seen, Munich.
Printed in Germany. Imprimé en Allemagne.

ISBN 3-932982-22-3

TREASURY OF THE RESIDENCE

The present collection of goldsmith's works, enamel, crystal and ivory works of the Munich Residence embodies three hundred years of history. In 1565 Duke Albrecht V of Bavaria decreed that particularly precious objects in his possession were to be gathered together and preserved as an inalienable treasure. They were to be kept, if possible for all time, in the Munich Residence (the "Neuveste") of the Wittelsbach family. This foundation of the first great art patron and collector of the House of Wittelsbach was enlarged by his son and grandson, Duke Wilhelm V and Elector Maximilian I through new acquisitions and treasures transferred from the "Kunstkammer" (collection of cabinet pieces) also founded by Albrecht V. The Electors Max Emanuel, Carl Albrecht and Max III Joseph continued to add to the collection. Elector Carl Theodor enlarged this collection in the late 18th century by transferring a major part of the "Palatine Treasury" from Heidelberg, Düsseldorf and Mannheim to Munich. The historical growth of this collection ended for the most part in the early 19th century with the addition of the regalia of the newly created Kingdom of Bavaria and a number of outstanding mediaeval works of art from secularised cathedral and monastery possessions.

As well as this secular Treasury, a collection of liturgical objects and reliquaries had been housed in the Residence in Munich since the early 17th century; these items had been acquired by Maximilian I for his newly founded Rich Chapel. The Wittelsbach rulers guarded these ecclesiastical possessions also as a treasure and in the period of secularisation extended the collection with sacred goldsmith's works from the Middle Ages.

Written instructions dated 1589 for the valet de chambre mentioned the "Treasure Tower" as the repository for the treasures. It is certain that this meant the "Silver Tower" of the mediaeval "Neuveste", which is known from contemporary illustrations. From 1733 the house treasury was displayed in a specially constructed cabinet (the current Porcelain Cabinet), which adjoined the Ancestral Gallery. In 1897 the collection was moved into a newly erected vault ("Old Treasury") and the general public was allowed limited access to it. Along with the first section of the redesigned Residence Museum after World War II, the Treasury was re-opened in its present form on 21 June 1958.

ROOM I

LATE GRAECO-ROMAN AND THE MIDDLE AGES

Several lapidary works originating in classical antiquity were used as ornamental stones in later goldsmith's works. Early mediaeval art is represented by the prayer book of Emperor Charles the Bald (Cat. 4), an altar ciborium (Cat. 5), and goldsmith's and lapidary works from the early 11th century. An onyx carving (Cat. 11) from the 13th century deserves particular mention as it represents the largest known example of an eagle cameo from the days of Hohenstaufen rulers. Three crowns from the 13th and 14th century are worth special attention.

1 RING: Gold, jasper. Carved gemstone (intaglio) from the time of the Roman Empire, 2nd – 3rd centuries AD. Mount, Italian, c.1530.

2 RING: Gold, onyx. Late Graeco-Roman, 3rd-4th centuries AD.

3 RING: Gold, garnet. Persian, 3rd-7th centuries AD (Sassanian dynasty 226 – 642).

4 PRAYERBOOK OF CHARLES THE BALD: Manuscript with miniature illuminations, probably Rheims, 846 – 869. Binding probably Munich, after 1635.

46 parchment sheets with gold lettering, decorative border, initial letters and double-page representation of "Emperor Charles the Bald praying before the Crucifix".

5 MINIATURE ALTAR CIBORIUM OF KING ARNULF OF CARINTHIA: Repoussé sheet gold, on oak, gold wire, precious stones, pearls. Probably Rheims, 890.

The ciborium is a representation in miniature of an early mediaeval baldachin over an altar. The actual portable altar is on the square pedastal slab. The altar ciborium was used as a portable altar. Figural repoussé decorations: on the tympana, symbols representing the Holy Trinity and angels; on the roof, scenes from the New Testament (the youth from Nain being raised from the dead, the prophecy of the Resurrection, Christ's First Temptation, Christ's Third Temptation, the appearance of the resurrected Christ at the Lake of Gennesaret, Christ's Second Temptation, the raising of Lazarus from the dead, the parable of the birds and the lilies). In the frame of the lower section the fragmentary dedication in repoussé majuscles.

◁ Cat. 5 Miniature altar ciborium
of King Arnulf of Carinthia, 890

Cat. 7 Two-handled cup (known as the "Henry Chalice"), 12th century

Cat. 9 Reliquary of Emperor Henry II, c.1020

6 SALVER: Brown flecked chalcedony. Probably Egyptian (Fatimite dynasty), c.1000.

7 TWO-HANDLED CUP (known as the "Henry Chalice"): Rock-crystal, silver-gilt, precious stones. Crystal: Fatimid, c.1000. Mount: probably German, 12th century.

8 CROSS OF QUEEN GISELA: Oak centre, cast gold, gold plate, gold cloisonné, precious stones, pearls, silk. Probably Regensburg, after 1006.

Donated by Queen Gisela of Hungary for the grave of her mother, Gisela of Burgundy, Duchess of Bavaria who died in 1006 and was buried in the Niedermünster in Regensburg. At Christ's feet the three-dimensional gold figures of Queen Gisela and her mother.

9 RELIQUARY OF EMPEROR HENRY II (cruciform reliquary): Oak, gold parcel-gilt, precious stones, rock-crystal, pearls, silk. Probably Metz or Reichenau, c.1010. Silver fitting on the back: presumably South German (Bamberg?), c.1020.

Reliquary for a splinter of the Cross. According to the inscription it was donated by Emperor Henry II to Bamberg Cathedral.

10 CROWN OF EMPRESS KUNIGUNDE: Gold, gold filigree, set with precious stones, pearls and glass pastes. Probably Lorraine (Metz?), c.1010–1020.

Tradition attributes this crown to Empress Kunigunde. A Gothic female crown (Cat. 15) was later mounted on the crown band; in 1931 the two were again separated.

11 BOX WITH HOHENSTAUFEN EAGLE CAMEO: Onyx, gold, silver-gilt, diamonds. Cameo: c.1230. Box: German (probably Vienna), c.1720.

From the estate of Empress Maria Amalia, the consort of Elector Carl Albrecht of Bavaria (1742–1745 as Emperor Karl VII).

12 PORTABLE ALTAR: Oak centre, silver-gilt, porphyry. South German (probably Regensburg), c.1240.

Second portable altar of the Arnulf ciborium (Cat. 5).

13 CROWN (known as "Henry's Crown"): Silver-gilt, precious stones, onyx cameos, pearls. South German or French, c.1280.

It is not certain whether the crown was originally used as part of the insignia. In the treasury of Bamberg Cathedral it was used as decoration on the head-reliquary of Emperor Henry II, who was canonized in 1146.

14 RING (known as the "Barbarossa Ring"): Gold, sapphire. French (?), probably towards 1200.

15 NOBLEWOMAN'S CROWN: Silver-gilt, gold, precious stones, pearls, gilded bronze. German or French, towards 1350 (with parts dating from around 1400 and the early 16th century).

United in the late Middle Ages with Cat. 10 to form a single crown, separated again in 1931.

16 CROWN OF AN ENGLISH QUEEN (known as the "Bohemian" or "Palatine" Crown): Gold, enamel, sapphires, rubies, emeralds, diamonds, pearls. Western Europe, c.1370–1380.

The crown was documented in 1399 in England as "older jewellery". It presumably comes from the possessions of King Edward III or Anna of Bohemia, the consort of King Richard II, who was deposed by Henry IV. Henry's daughter, Princess Blanche, became the consort of Palatine Elector Ludwig III in 1402 and brought the crown into the "Palatine Treasury" as part of her dowry.

◁ Cat. 10 Crown of Empress
Kunigunde, c.1010–1020

Cat. 18 Ostrich-egg cup, c.1410–1420

LATE GOTHIC AND EARLY RENAISSANCE

The 15th century is represented predominantly by works of sacred art. In addition to a Burgundian portrait medaillion and a probably French prayer chain, German, Flemish and Italian works are exhibited.
In the first half of the 16th century, the Renaissance extended also to areas north of the Alps, giving new content to works of art, although late Gothic forms still continued to have an influence.

17   PENDANT with Christ represented as the Man of Sorrows: Gold, partly enamelled, rock-crystal, pearls. Probably Paris, towards 1400.

18   OSTRICH-EGG CUP: Ostrich-egg, silver-gilt. Probably French or German, c.1410 – 1420.

19   PORTRAIT MEDALLION (pendant): Gold, partly enamelled, chalcedony. Burgundy, c.1440.

The person depicted is most probably Duke Philip the Good of Burgundy, who was a guest of the Bavarian dukes in 1454.

20   KNIFE: Rock-crystal handle. Mount: silver-gilt. German, c.1450.

21   DECADE ROSARY: Gold, enamel. French Burgundian, c.1450 – 1460.

On both sides of the gold hearts are representations of scenes from the history of Saints Joachim and Anna and from the life of the Virgin.

22   PILGRIM'S FLASK: Onyx. Mount: gold, enamel. Probably Burgundian, 15th century, but possibly older, late Graeco-Roman or Fatimid. Mount: probably Munich, c.1570 – 1580.

23   ROUND BOWL (known as the "Wolfgang Bowl"): Grained cherry-wood, silver, enamel. Probably Regensburg, c.1460 – 1470. Enamel platter: Rhenish?, probably older.

Legend connects this bowl with Bishop Wolfgang of Regensburg (d. 994).

24   BEAKER AND COVER: Red jasper, silver-gilt mount, diamonds, garnets, amethysts. Probably German, 15th century. Mount: c.1670.

25   STATUETTE OF ST LAWRENCE: Silver, repoussé, parcel-gilt. Northern Netherlands or Lower Rhine, c.1490.

Cat. 28 Rosary bead, Flemish, c.1500

26   GLASS CUP: Glass, silver-gilt. Venetian, c.1500. Mount: German, 1643.

27   CUP: Silver-gilt, narwal bone panels, ostrich-egg cover. Nuremberg, c.1500. Cover: c.1530–1540.

The medallion (Matthes Gebel, Nuremberg 1528) shows a portrait of the Palatine Count Ottheinrich, later Palatine Elector.

28   ROSARY BEAD: Boxwood, gold, enamel. Flemish, c.1500. Enamel base: Munich, c.1600.

The carvings on the inner surfaces depict scenes from the Life of Christ.

29   ROSARY BEAD: Boxwood. Flemish, c.1500.

According to tradition a monk called Hieronymus Faber (from Messina) worked on this carving for 18 years. The relief carvings on the inner surfaces depict the Stations of the Cross and the Crucifixion.

30   ROSARY BEAD: Boxwood, leather. Flemish, c.1500.

The carving depicts the Adoration of the Shepherds and Adoration of the Magi.

31   ROSARY BEAD: Boxwood, ivory. Probably Flemish, c.1500.

Hemisphere with carving of the Adoration of the Magi.

32   CHALICE: Gold, partly enamelled, pearls, rubies. German, before 1514.

The chalice belonged to the Archbishop of Mainz, Albrecht of Brandenburg.

33   SALVER: Silver, lightly gilded, rock-crystal, rubies, sapphires. Valerio Belli, Venice or Padua, c.1520.

The salver may have been a gift from Pope Leo X to Duke Wilhelm IV of Bavaria (1508–1550).

34   PILGRIM'S FLASK: Agate. Mount: silver-gilt. German (?), c.1520.

35   PENDANT CROSS: Silver-gilt. South-west German (?), c.1520.

36   MADONNA AND CHILD: Silver-gilt, copper-gilt. South German (probably Regensburg), c.1520. Nimbus: 17th century.

37   CUP: Silver-gilt. Antwerp, c.1530.

On the base, cup walls and lid: repoussé and richly engraved multifigured depictions from the life of the inhabitants of the recently discovered America.

38 CUP (decorated with coins): Silver, mostly silver-gilt. Strasbourg, c.1530–1535.

On the knop is a sitting lion with the coat-of-arms of Bavaria and of the Palatinate. The cup is decorated with casts of Roman coins (2nd–3rd centuries).

39 CHALICE: Agate. Mount: gold, partly enamelled, diamonds, rubies, pearls. Melchior Baier the Elder, Nuremberg, 1536.

On the base are six medallion portraits of the members of the family of Margrave Georg of Brandenburg, for whom the chalice was made.

40 BOWL AND COVER (known as the "Holbein Bowl"): Rock-crystal, gold, enamel, diamonds, rubies, emeralds, pearls. Rock crystal bowl: 14th century. Mount: design by Hans Holbein the Younger, probably French workmanship, c.1540.

The bowl was last mentioned in 1649 in the Tower of London.

41–42 TWO CRUETS FOR MASS: Gold, partly enamelled, set with cameos. German (Mainz?), 1514–1545, further work c.1700.

Belonged to Cardinal Albrecht, Margrave of Brandenburg, Elector of Mainz. Later came into the possession of Elector Lothar Franz von Schönborn (coat-of-arms on the top of the lid).

43 RAPPOLTSTEIN CUP: Silver-gilt, partly enamelled. Georg Kobenhaupt, Strasbourg, c.1555.

Mining scenes and coat-of-arms refer to the silver mines of the Lords of Rappoltstein.

44 LADLE: Silver-gilt. German, c.1550.

Belongs to the Rappoltstein Cup (Cat. 43).

45 SHALLOW BOWL: Silver-gilt, partly enamelled. Melchior Baier the Elder, Nuremberg, c.1545.

Belonged to the Polish Princess Anna Catharina Constanza, the daughter of King Sigismund III of Poland. Later she married Palatinate Elector Philipp Wilhelm. In the centre of the bowl is a relief depicting Christ in the Pharisee's house (after an engraving by Marcantonio Raimondi).

46 SPOON OF A CHALICE: Gold. Probably South German, mid 16th century.

Cat. 43 Rappoltstein cup,
G. Kobenhaupt, c.1555 ▷

47 JEWEL CASKET: Silver-gilt, partly enamelled, diamonds, rubies, emeralds. Italian, towards 1550.

This casket is one of the first seventeen objects donated in 1565 by Duke Albrecht V of Bavaria to the Treasury.

48 PENDANT (small whistle): Soapstone. Mount: gold, enamel. Italian, c.1550.

49 DOUBLE-HEADED EAGLE: Gold, enamel, diamonds, rubies, pearls. Vienna or Italy, c.1550.

Belonged to Duchess Anna, daughter of Emperor Ferdinand I and wife of Duke Albrecht V.

50 PENDANT: Diamonds in gold mount. Italian, c.1550 (base probably Munich, c.1640).

With IHS monogram in fractur of the name of Jesus. According to an inventory dated 1572, Duke Wilhelm V is said to have worn the gem daily.

51 RING : Gold, partly enamelled, emerald. Gem carving: perhaps Burgundian, 14th/15th centuries. Mount: Italian, c.1550.

The ring comes from the estate of Empress Maria Amalia, consort of Elector Carl Albrecht (1742–1745 as Emperor Karl VII).

52 JEWISH RITUAL RING: Gold, German (?), c.1500.

The ring is the oldest known example of a Jewish wedding ring. It was not intended to be worn, but was part of the Jewish wedding ritual. The building represents the destroyed temple in Jerusalem and the home the bridal pair are to set up together. The inscription reads "masel tauw" ("Good Luck").

53 RING: Gold, engraved carnelian (intaglio). Italian, c.1530–1540.

54 RING: Gold, engraved sapphire (intaglio). Gem carving: Italian, c.1530–1540. Mount: German, c.1700.

55 "WEDDING RING" OF DUKE ALBRECHT V OF BAVARIA (more probably ring of Duke Albrecht IV): Gold, partly enamelled, diamonds. German, late 15th century.

56 RING: Gold, chrysoberyl. Italian, c.1550.

STATUETTE OF ST GEORGE AND ORNATE CHAIN

57 ORNATE CHAIN: Gold, enamel, emeralds (copies), spinels, diamonds, pearls. Munich, towards 1575, probably after a design by Hans Mielich.

The chain was worn in the 19th century by the Bavarian Kings in their role as Grand Masters of the Order at the ceremonies of the Knights of St George.

58 STATUETTE OF ST GEORGE: Gold, enamel, silver-gilt, diamonds, rubies, emeralds, opals, agate, chalcedony, rock-crystal and other precious stones, pearls. Munich, between 1586 and 1597, probably after a design by Friedrich Sustris; the workmanship is ascribed to various master craftsmen in Augsburg and Munich. The base was remodelled between 1638 and 1641.

The George statuette was created as a reliquary for a St George relic, which Archbishop Ernst of Cologne sent in 1586 to his brother Duke Wilhelm V of Munich. In the 17th century, the statuette was displayed at major holidays on the altar of the Rich Chapel. The armour of the statuette was modelled on the state armour worn by Wilhelm V for Corpus Christi processions; the bearded face of the Saint behind the movable helmet visor resembles that of the statuette's patron, Duke Wilhelm V (boxwood).

Cat. 64 Image of Virgin (icon), Moscow/Munich, 16th century

RELIGIOUS ART

The "Secret Chamber Chapel" ("Rich Chapel") erected by Maximilian I in 1607 was the centre of an extensive collection of relics, paraments and altar utensils. The relics and a part of the parament collections have been displayed since 1958 in the Residence Museum. The other sacred objects have been incorporated into the Treasury along with items from the Court Chapel and the Church of All Saints. The house altar commissioned by Albrecht V and his consort Anna of Austria is of great importance, since it became the model for further small altars from the era of Wilhelm V (Cat. 59). Deserving special notice from the works of the early 17th century are ivory sculptures by Christoph Angermair and Georg Petel, as well as one of the earliest monstrances with nimbus (Cat. 104), probably made in Munich, and valuable altar utensils from the 18th century.

Liturgical Items

59 PRIVATE ALTAR OF DUKE ALBRECHT V OF BAVARIA: Ebony, gold, enamel. Ascribed to Abraham I Lotter and David Altenstetter, Augsburg, 1573–1574. Casing: Hans Krieger, Augsburg, at around the same time.

Predella frieze: Adam and Eve in Paradise before and after the Fall; Cornice: Resurrection of Christ. On the side wings St Albrecht and St Anna as patron saints of Duke Albrecht and his wife. The original pietà of the middle niche was lost and replaced by fittings from the back wall of the altar.

60 SMALL PRIVATE ALTAR WITH ADORATION OF THE MAGI: Ebony, gold, enamel, rubies, emeralds, diamonds and other precious stones. Ascribed to Ulrich Eberlin, Augsburg, c.1575-1580.

Private altar of Duke Wilhelm V.

61 SMALL PRIVATE ALTAR WITH SCOURGING OF CHRIST: Ebony, gold, enamel, rubies, emeralds, diamonds and other precious stones, pearls. Ascribed to Ulrich Eberlin, Augsburg, c.1575–1585.

Private altar of Duke Wilhlem V.

62 SMALL PRIVATE ALTAR WITH ADORATION OF THE MAGI: Ebony, gold, enamel, silver. Augsburg, towards 1600. Casing of baldachin: c.1750.

63 SMALL PRIVATE ALTAR WITH ENTHRONED VIRGIN AND CHILD: Ebony, ivory, wax, gold, enamel, rubies, emeralds, diamonds, pearls. Probably after a design by Hans Krumper, Munich, c.1600.

64 IMAGE OF VIRGIN (icon): Wooden panel; cast, chased and gilded sheet silver; pearls, precious stones. Probably Moscow, 16th century. Crown: Munich, c.1580.

Probably a copy of the Miraculous Image at Smolensk.

65 RELIQUARY: Cast silver-gilt. Moscow, 1602.

Tradition has it that the reliquary was made in 1602 for Czar Boris Fedorowitsch and his son, Fedor. In 1614 King Sigismund III of Poland gave it as a gift to Duke Wilhelm V of Munich.

66 CRUCIFIX: Ebony, gold, enamel, diamonds, rubies, emeralds, pearls. Hans Reimer, Munich, c.1570.

A gift from Duchess Anna of Austria, wife of Duke Albrecht V, to Andechs monastery.

67 STANDING CROSS: Cast silver-gilt, glass. South German (probably Regensburg), c.1580–1590.

68 CRUCIFIX: Ebony, gold, enamel, silver, precious stones, pearls. Munich or Augsburg, 1623–1626.

Commissioned by Maximilian I of Bavaria (r. 1597–1651, from 1623 Elector).

69 CRUCIFIX: Limewood, tortoiseshell. South German (Augsburg) or Italian, first half of 17th century.

70 CRUCIFIX: Mother-of-pearl, carnelians, diamonds, silver-gilt. German, c.1720.

71 CHRIST CARRYING THE CROSS (relief): Gold, ebony. Munich, 1598.

72 GLORIFICATION OF THE VIRGIN (relief after a painting by Christoph Schwarz): Gold, ebony. Munich, probably 1598.

73–74 THE ANNUNCIATION AND THE VISITATION (reliefs): Silver, ebony, velvet. South German, c.1610–1620.

75 THE DESCENT FROM THE CROSS (known as the "Michelangelo Relief"): Wax on black slate. Johann de Voss (after Italian model), Augsburg, c.1610.

76 PILLAR WITH FIGURE OF EMPEROR HENRY II (formerly a reliquary): Ebony, rock-crystal, enamel, cameos, agate. South German, (probably Augsburg), c.1575–1580.

77 CHRIST SCOURGED AT THE PILLAR (formerly a reliquary): Ebony, rock-crystal, gold, enamel, silver-gilt, precious stones. South German (probably Augsburg), c.1575–1580. Base stand: early 17th century.

78 SMALL FIGURE OF VIRGIN: Mother-of-pearl, silver-gilt, brilliants, precious stones. Dutch (?), 17th century.

79 MARY'S COLUMN: Gold, enamel, silver-gilt, rubies, turquoises, rock-crystal. German, c.1660–1670.

80 MINIATURE ALTAR: Silver-gilt, gold, silver, enamel, precious stones. German, c.1700.

81 ARMA CHRISTI (Cross and Instruments of Passion): Gold, enamel, silver-gilt, rock-crystal, diamonds, rubies. German, c. 1720.

Ecclesiastical vessels and ornaments

82 OSCULATORIUM ("Instrumentum Pacis"): Ebony, gold, enamel. Augsburg, c.1576–1580.

83 OSCULATORIUM ("Instrumentum Pacis"): Gold, enamel, diamonds, rubies, chalcedony. Augsburg, c.1580.

84 OSCULATORIUM ("Instrumentum Pacis"): Ebony, gold, enamel, emeralds. Augsburg, c.1580–1585.

85–86 TWO SMALL VASES: Rock-crystal, gold, enamel, rose quartz. Munich, c.1590.

87–88 TWO CANDLESTICKS: Gold. Munich, c.1590.

89–94 SIX CANDLESTICKS: Silver-gilt. Philipp I Warnberger, Augsburg, c.1585–1590.

95–96 TWO CANDLESTICKS: Silver-gilt, chased. Nikolaus Emmerling, Nuremberg, c.1590.

97 PYX (receptacle for the Host): Silver-gilt. Nikolaus Emmerling, Nuremberg, c.1590.

98 CIBORIUM: Silver-gilt. Regensburg, 1591.

99–101 THREE CANON TABLETS: Silver-gilt, pergament. Gregor Bair, Jacob Schenauer, Christoph Lencker, Augsburg, c.1585–1590.

The three canon tablets originate from the altar in the Rich Chapel in the Munich Residence.

102–103 ASPERSORIUM WITH SPRINKLER: Silver-gilt. Philipp I Warnberger, Augsburg, c.1585–1590.

104 MONSTRANCE WITH NIMBUS: Gold. Munich (?), c.1600.

Earliest known German example of monstrance with nimbus.

105–106 TWO CONSECRATED HAND-BELLS: Silver, cast and chased. Abraham Zeggin, Munich, c.1600.

107 MISSAL: Silver, chased. Munich, 1613. Printing: Nikolaus Heinrich. Binding: at the same time or a little later.

108–113 CROSS, TWO CANDLESTICKS, TWO CRUETS AND STAND: Rock-crystal, silver. Probably German, 17th century.

Equipment for a small private altar.

114–116 ALTAR CROSS AND TWO CANDLESTICKS: Rock-crystal, gold, silver, enamel, emeralds, rubies. Italian or German, early 17th century.

117–118 BAPTISMAL FONT AND FLAGON: Silver-gilt. Munich or Augsburg, c.1620.

119 BOOK BINDING: Silver, parcel-gilt. Johann Andreas Thelott, Augsburg, c.1695.

From the estate of King Otto of Bavaria (d. 1916).

120 VIATICUM SET: Silver-gilt. German, 1704.

121 TROWEL: Silver-gilt. Rome, 1825.

The trowel was used in 1825 by Pope Leo XII at the ceremonial closing up of the Porta Santa in St Peter's in Rome.

122 BAPTISMAL SHELL: Silver-gilt. Munich, 19th century.

Cat. 104 Monstrance with nimbus,
Munich (?), c.1600 ▷

Cat. 156 Golgotha, ivory relief, Chr. Angermair, Munich, 1631

123–124 CHALICE AND PATEN: Silver-gilt. South German, c.1600.

125–126 CHALICE AND PATEN: Gold, partly enamelled. Christoph Ulrich Eberl, Munich, 1624.

127–128 CHALICE AND PATEN: Silver-gilt. Master's mark "AH" (?), Regensburg (?), 1702.

129–131 CHALICE, PATEN AND SPOON: Silver-gilt, precious stones. Rhenish, c.1710.

132–134 CHALICE, PATEN AND SPOON: Silver, parcel-gilt. Master's mark "IL", Mainz (?), c.1710.

135–137 CHALICE, PATEN AND SPOON: Silver, parcel-gilt. Augsburg (?), c.1750.

138–139 CHALICE AND PATEN: Silver, parcel-gilt. Ignaz Franzowitz, Munich, c.1780.

140–141 TWO CRUETS FOR MASS: Silver-gilt. Munich or Augsburg, c.1620.

142–144 TWO CRUETS FOR MASS AND STAND: Silver, parcel-gilt. Franz Ignaz Berdolt, Augsburg, c.1730.

145–147 TWO CRUETS FOR MASS AND STAND: Silver, parcel-gilt. Master's mark "AS", Munich, 1756.

148–150 TWO CRUETS FOR MASS AND STAND: Silver-gilt. Ignaz Franzowitz, Munich, 1782.

Ivories, amber and coral work

151 THE CHRIST CHILD DISPENSING BLESSING (Salvator mundi): Ivory, ebony, silver-gilt. Hans Krumper, Munich, c.1620.

152 FIGURE OF ST SEBASTIAN UNDER A BALDACHIN: Ivory, coral. South German (probably Munich), c.1620.

153 FIGURE OF ST SEBASTIAN: Ivory, coral, ebony. Leonhard Kern, South German, c.1625.

154 OUR LADY OF SORROWS: Ivory, ebony. Christoph Angermair, Munich, c.1630.

155 THE SCOURGING OF CHRIST: Ivory. Christoph Angermair, Munich, c.1630.

156 GOLGOTHA (relief): Ivory. Christoph Angermair, Munich, 1631.

157 CRUCIFIX: Ivory, black-stained wood. Georg Petel, Augsburg, c.1630.

Figure of Christ carved from one piece of ivory, modelled on a type created by Peter Paul Rubens.

158 CRUCIFIX: Ivory, ebony, rosewood. Corpus Christi: ascribed to Georg Petel, Augsburg, c.1628–1629. Base and stem of cross: Georg Sebastian Gugelhör, Munich, 1767.

159 CRUCIFIX: Ivory, rosewood and palisander. Corpus Christi: ascribed to Georg Petel, Augsburg, c.1623–1624. Base and stem of cross: Georg Sebastian Gugelhör, Munich, 1767.

The alliance coat-of-arms refers to Elector Max III Joseph of Bavaria and his consort, Maria Anna of Saxony.

160 CRUCIFIX: Ivory, rosewood. Corpus Christi: Munich, c.1725. Base and stem of cross: Georg Sebastian Gugelhör, Munich, c.1725.

161 CRUCIFIXION GROUP: Amber. East Prussia, second half of 17th century.

162–165 ADORATION OF THE SHEPHERDS AND ADORA-TION OF THE MAGI, CROWN OF THORNS AND ECCE HOMO (reliefs in box frame): Ivory. Circles around the workshop of the Dominican Steinhardt, Munich, c.1700. Frame: c.1725.

166 STONING OF ST STEPHEN (relief in box frame): Probably circles around the Steinhardt workshop, Munich, c.1700. Frame: c.1725.

167–168 CHRIST WASHING HIS DISCIPLES' FEET AND THE LAST SUPPER (reliefs in box frame): Ivory. Munich, c.1720.

169–170 CHRIST CARRYING THE CROSS AND CHRIST BEING NAILED TO THE CROSS (reliefs in box frame): Ivory. Munich, c.1720.

171 CORONATION OF MARY (relief in box frame): Ivory. Munich, c.1730.

172 THE MAN OF SORROWS (relief): Ivory. Munich, c.1730.

The counterpart (Mourning Mary with John) is in the Bavarian National Museum in Munich.

173 ADORATION OF THE SHEPHERDS: Ivory, ebony. German (Saxony?), early 19th century.

Cat. 157 Crucifix, Georg Petel,
Augsburg, c.1630 ▷

174 HOLY WATER STOUP: Agate, rock-crystal, gold, enamel. North Italian, second half of 16th century.

175 SMALL PRAYER BOOK: Binding: gold, enamel. Italian, c.1571.

176 PENDANT in the form of a small triptych: Gold, enamel. French, 1572.

177 CALVARY: Gold, partly enamelled, rubies, emeralds, stalactites. German, c.1580.

178 PENDANT (Virgin): Gold, enamel, rubies, diamond. South German (Regensburg?), c.1590.

179–180 TWO BOXES AND LIDS (formerly reliquaries): Gold, enamel, precious stones, glass. Ascribed to Ulrich Eberlin, Augsburg, c.1592.

181 SMALL FIGURE OF A NUN: Casing: Silver-gilt, partly enamelled, diamonds, glass. Statuette: gypsum, painted. German, 17th century.

182 ST WOLFANG'S AXE: Silver-gilt. German, 17th century.

183 PECTORAL CROSS: Gold, silver, diamonds. South German, 17th century.

184 PENDANT (St Anthony): Chased gold, Italian (?), 17th century.

185 PENDANT: Coral, gold, enamel. Munich or Augsburg, c.1620.

186–187 TWO PRAYER-BOOK COVERS: Ivory, shell, coral, silver-gilt, enamel, emeralds. Augsburg, first half of 17th century. Border: towards 1660.

188 PRAYER BOOK: Gold, partly enamelled, diamonds. Munich or Augsburg, c.1620.

189 ROSARY BEAD: Wood, gold filigree. German, c.1620.

190 SMALL PRAYER BOOK: Heliotrope, gold, enamel, rubies, opals. French, towards 1650.

191 FRAMED CAMEO with "St Veronica's veil": Silver-gilt, enamel, precious stones. Augsburg (?), second half of 17th century.

192 CAMEO IN STANDING FRAME with heads of Christ and Mary: Heliotrope. Frame: silver-gilt, precious stones. Augsburg (?), c.1660–1670.

193 PENDANT SHOWING MINIATURES ("Angel appearing to Mary"): Gold, diamonds, garnets. Frame: German, c.1680. Miniature paintings: c.1600.

194 PENDANT SHOWING MINIATURES ("Angel appearing to Mary"): Silver-gilt, diamonds. Frame: German, c.1680. Miniature paintings: c.1600.

195 LOCKET CONTAINING MINIATURE PORTRAITS: Copper-gilt. Munich, c.1685.

Allegorical portraits of Elector Max Emanuel and his consort, Maria Antonia as St John and Maria Immaculata. Probably a gift from the Bavarian Elector and his consort to the Palatine Elector Johann Wilhelm and Anna Maria, his consort.

196 PENDANT (cross): Rock-crystal, gold. Italian, c.1700.

197 PENDANT (cross): Gold, rose quartz, diamonds, silver. German, 17th/18th centuries.

198 OVAL MEDALLION ("Wessobrunn Madonna"): Parchment, silver, parcel-gilt, glass. South German, mid 18th century.

199 DIPTYCH IN EGG FORM ("Easter Egg"): Salzburg alabaster, gold mount. South German, 18th century.

Highly sculptured interior surfaces: the Lamb of the Apocalypse and the Risen Christ.

200–203 FOUR MEDALS ("anno santo 1775"): Silver. Rome, 1775.

The Latin texts relate to the opening and closing of the Holy Portals of the four patriarchal basilicas in Rome.

204   ROSARY: Lapis lazuli, gold, pearls, silk. German, c.1590.

205–207   THREE ROSARIES: Heliotrope, rose quartz, emerald, diamonds, glass, gold. German, c.1600.

208   ROSARY: Lapis lazuli, gold, parchment. German, c.1690.

209   ROSARY: Heliotrope, ivory, silver-gilt. German, c.1720.

210   ROSARY: Silver-gilt filigree, glass. Probably Italian, 17th/18th centuries.

211   ROSARY: Bavarian pearls, coral, gold. South German, 17th/18th centuries.

212   ROSARY: Alabaster, silver-gilt, glass, parchment. Probably South German, 18th century.

213 ROSARY: Onyx, silver-gilt. 18th century.

214   DECADE ROSARY: Carved apricot stones, gold, pearls. Italian, c.1560.

215   DECADE   ROSARY: Ambergris, gold enamel, wood. Munich, c.1590.

216   DECADE ROSARY: Onyx, gold, ruby, pearls, chalcedony. German, 17th century.

217–218   TWO DECADE ROSARIES: Lapis lazuli, gold, passementerie work. German, 17th century.

219–220   TWO DECADE ROSARIES: Heliotrope, gold, silver. German, first half of 17th century.

221   DECADE ROSARY: Agate, gold, gold enamel. German, c.1650.

222–229   EIGHT DECADE ROSARIES: Yellow to red agate, glass, silver, silk. 17th/18th centuries.

230–231   TWO DECADE ROSARIES: Jasper, silver-gilt filigree, agate, silver, glass. 18th century.

ROOM V

INSIGNIA AND ORDERS

Regalia were intended as symbols of the dignity and power of a ruler. The most revered of these, the crown, remained for one and a half millenia the most important symbol of sovereignty; the sceptre, sword, imperial orb and other items accompanied it.

Soon after the founding of the spiritual orders and chivalric fraternities, "orders" came into being, i.e. distinctions awarded for certain merits.

232 FRANCONIAN DUKE'S SWORD: Silver-gilt, niello, steel, velvet. Probably Franconia, c.1455–1460.

This magnificent weapon was the ceremonial sword of Prince-Bishop Johann III von Grumbach, Duke of Franconia (1455–1466). It can be assumed that it was the great symbol of sovereignty for the secular power of the Würzburg prince-bishops; presumably it was also accorded the character of an executioner's sword.

233 SWORD OF DUKE CHRISTOPH OF BAVARIA: Silver, parcel-gilt, rubies. German or North Italian, c.1480.

The sword was probably a gift from Queen Beatrix of Hungary, wife of Matthias Corvinus, to the Bavarian Duke. It was used by the Bavarian rulers as Grand Masters of the Order of the Knights of Saint George, when knighting new members of the Order.

234 PALATINE SWORD: Silver-gilt, partly enamelled, steel. Abraham I Drentwett, Augsburg, c.1653.

Coat-of-arms of the Palatinate with device of the Order of the Garter. Comissioned by Karl I Ludwig, Palatine Elector. From 1745 it became the ceremonial sword of the Order of the Knights of St Hubertus.

235 GOLDEN ROSE: Gold, sapphire. Probably Rome, 1562.

The Golden Rose or Rose of Virtue was originally awarded to papal officials, later also to princes. Given by Pope Pius IV to Duchess Anna, wife of Duke Albrecht V of Bavaria.

236 GOLDEN ROSE: Gold, sapphire. Probably Rome, 1635.

Given by Pope Urban VIII to Maria Anna, during her engagement to become the second consort of Maximilian I of Bavaria.

237 KNEE BUCKLE OF THE ORDER OF THE GARTER: Velvet, gold, partly enamelled, diamonds. England, c.1612.

Belonged to Friedrich V, Palatine Elector (known as the "Winter King"), who was awarded this English order, the Order of St George (otherwise known as the Order of the Garter) on 7 December 1612, on the occasion of his marriage to Princess Elisabeth, daughter of King James I of England.

238 IMPERIAL ORB: Gold, sapphires, emeralds, rubies, spinets, diamonds. Probably Augsburg, 1619.

Probably made by order of Friedrich V, Palatine Elector, on the occasion of his coronation as King of Bohemia in Prague on 4 November 1619. The imperial orb is also the symbol of the imperial archdapifer. In 1623 this office passed from the Palatine Electorate to the Electorate of Bavaria.

239–242 COPIES OF THE OTTONIAN IMPERIAL INSIGNIA

Made for the coronation of Carl Albrecht, Elector of Bavaria, as Holy Roman Emperor (12 February 1742). The insignia were formerly richly set with precious stones but these were removed under Elector Max III Joseph and incorporated into various items of jewellery.

239 EMPEROR'S CROWN (jewels removed): Silver-gilt. Philip Jakob VI Drentwett, Augsburg, probably 1742.

240 EMPEROR'S CROWN (jewels removed): Silver-gilt. Nikolaus Nell, Frankfurt, 1742.

241–242 SCEPTRE AND IMPERIAL ORB: Silver-gilt, quartz. Frankfurt or Augsburg, probably 1742.

243–244 LEGION OF HONOUR RAPIER AND BANDOLEER: Gold, steel, tortoiseshell; gold embroidery on grey velvet. Martin-Guillaume Biennais and St Etienne, Paris, 1804.

The sword is the emblem for membership of the Legion of Honour. It is uncertain whether it was a present from Napoleon to Elector Max IV Joseph, or whether it came from the estate of Eugène Beauharnais, Napoleon's stepson and son-in-law of Max IV Joseph.

245–251 CROWN INSIGNIA OF THE KINGDOM OF BAVARIA: Gold, silver, parcel-gilt, steel, diamonds and brilliants, rubies, emeralds, sapphires, pearls, gold embroidery, enamel. Martin-Guillaume Biennais and workshop, Paris, 1806–1807.

After Napoleon I was crowned Emperor on 2 December 1804, and after the Battle of Austerlitz and the Treaty of Pressburg (26 December 1805), Elector Max IV Joseph proclaimed himself King of Bavaria as Max I Joseph, on 1 January 1806. The crown insignia were ordered from Napoleon's court goldsmiths in Paris. The design follows drawings by the Parisian architect, Charles Percier. The insignia rest on one of the presentation cushions also specially made in Paris. The Bavarian crown insignia were not worn by the ruler, but were carried or placed before him on cushions at ceremonial occasions in the Throne Room of the Residence. The Queen's crown was altered by the Munich court jeweller Gottfried Merk in 1867 on the orders of King Ludwig II.

◁ Cat. 233 Sword of Duke Christoph
of Bavaria, c.1480

245 THE KING'S CROWN

246 THE QUEEN'S CROWN

247 THE BAVARIAN IMPERIAL ORB

248 THE BAVARIAN SCEPTRE

249 THE BAVARIAN SWORD

250 SHOULDER BELT OF THE BAVARIAN SWORD

251 BOX FOR SEALS

252 PEARL DIADEM: Pearls, gold, brilliants. Perhaps Caspar Rieländer, probably Munich, c.1825.

From the estate of King Otto of Greece.

253–254 TWO EARRINGS: Pearls, silver-gilt, brilliants. Caspar Rieländer, Munich, 1825.

255–261 RUBY JEWELS OF QUEEN THERESE (diadem, necklace, brooch, two earrings, two bracelets): Gold, silver, rubies, spinels, brilliants. Caspar Rieländer, Munich, 1830.

Commissioned by King Ludwig I for Therese, his consort. Most of the gemstones come from the "Old Ruby Jewels" of Elector Max III Joseph.

INSIGNIA OF THE ORDER OF THE KNIGHTS OF ST GEORGE

In 1496 Duke Albrecht IV of Bavaria set up an order for "the court, the court servants, knights, counts and barons". Elector Carl Albrecht (r. 1726-1745) changed the order into an Order of Knights on 24 April 1729. The initials IVPF and VIBI on the cross refer to the mottos of the order: "Justus ut palma florebit" (The righteous shall flourish like a palm tree) and "Virgini immaculate Bavaria immaculata" (To the Immaculate Virgin, immaculate Bavaria). Only state insignia are exhibited.

262–265 GARNITURE OF THE ORDER OF ST GEORGE ("jewel" cross, star, hat-brooch, brooch): Rubies, diamonds and brilliants, glass pastes in silver-gilt mounts. Probably Daniel Gouers (Govaers), Paris, towards 1729.

The ensemble of insignia was commissioned by Elector Carl Albrecht, probably on the occasion of the refounding of the Order.

Cat. 255 Diadem of Queen Therese, C. Rieländer, Munich, 1830 ▷

266–269 GARNITURE OF THE ORDER OF ST GEORGE (cross, star, hat-brooch, brooch): Emeralds, rubies, brilliants, glass pastes in silver-gilt and partly enamelled mounts. Perhaps Daniel Gouers (Govaers), Paris, c.1729.

270–272 GARNITURE OF THE ORDER OF ST GEORGE (cross, star, hat-brooch): Brilliants, rubies and glass pastes in enamelled, silver-gilt mounts. Perhaps Daniel Gouers (Govaers), Paris, c.1729.

273–274 PARTS OF A GARNITURE OF THE ORDER OF ST GEORGE (hat-brooch, ribbon-brooch): Rubies, brilliants, silver-gilt mounts. Munich, c.1760.

275 CHAIN OF THE ORDER OF ST GEORGE (fragment): Fire-gilded bronze, cold painting. German, 18th century.

276–279 GARNITURE OF THE ORDER OF ST GEORGE (cross, star, hat-brooch, shoulder-ribbon): Emeralds, rubies, brilliants, glass pastes in partly enamelled, silver-gilt mounts. Munich, c.1830.

280–281 GARNITURE OF THE ORDER OF ST GEORGE (cross, star): Rubies, brilliants, glass pastes in silver-gilt mounts. Munich, c.1830.

282 STAR OF THE ORDER OF THE KNIGHTS OF ST GEORGE: Rubies, brilliants and blue glass pastes in silver-gilt mounts. Gottfried Merk, Munich, 1869.

The star of the Order was made for King Ludwig II of Bavaria (r. 1864–1886).

283 RAPIER OF THE ORDER OF ST GEORGE: Silver, partly enamelled, steel, mother-of-pearl, parchment. Johann Stroblberger, Munich, probably c.1870.

284–287 GARNITURE OF THE ORDER OF ST GEORGE (cross, star, hat-brooch, shoulder-ribbon): Gold, partly enamelled, rubies, diamonds and brilliants, emeralds, peridots (chrysolites). Adam Hausinger, Munich, 1874.

288–289 GARNITURE OF THE ORDER OF ST GEORGE (cross, star): Rubies, brilliants and glass pastes in silver-gilt mounts. Gottfried Merk, Munich, 1902.

290–291 GARNITURE OF THE ORDER OF ST GEORGE (cross, star): Rubies, brilliants and glass pastes in silver-gilt mounts. Gottfried Merk, Munich, 1905.

INSIGNIA OF THE ORDER OF THE KNIGHTS OF ST HUBERTUS

The Family Order of the Palatine Wittelsbachs is traced back to a foundation by Gerhard II, Duke of Jülich and Berg, after the Battle of Linnich on 3 November 1444. Palatine Elector Johann Wilhelm re-instituted the order on 29 September 1708, and it was confirmed for the last time on 18 May 1808 by King Max I Joseph of Bavaria. In Traw vast (staunch in loyalty) is the device of the order.

Only state insignia from the Order of the Knights of St Hubertus are exhibited.

292 HERALD'S STAFF: Silver-gilt, partly enamelled; enamelled copper, wood, velvet, pearls. Augsburg or Heidelberg, towards 1708.

The matching heraldic robes are kept in the Bavarian Army Museum in Ingolstadt.

293–294 TWO CHAINS OF THE ORDER OF ST HUBERTUS: Gold, partly enamelled. Probably Mannheim or Heidelberg, towards 1708.

295–296 GARNITURE OF THE ORDER OF ST HUBERTUS (cross, star): Diamonds and brilliants, silver-gilt mounts, gold. Probably Heidelberg, 1708.

297–298 GARNITURE OF THE ORDER OF ST HUBERTUS (cross, star): Gold, silver, parcel-gilt and enamelled, emeralds, brilliants. Mannheim, towards 1708. New mount: probably Maria Cordula von Pigage, 1761.

299 BOOK OF GOSPELS OF THE ORDER OF THE KNIGHTS OF ST HUBERTUS: Parchment, wood and snake-skin, enamelled gold fittings. Heinrich Tesch, Düsseldorf, 1709. Binding with fittings: probably Peter Boy the Elder, c.1600 and 1727.

300 RELIEF WITH PICTURE OF ST HUBERTUS: Silver, mat and polished repoussé. Georg Lorenz II Gaap, Augsburg, c.1708–1710.

St Hubertus bears the features of Palatine Elector Johann Wilhelm (r. 1690–1716), who re-instituted the Order of St Hubertus in 1708.

301 CROSIER OF THE PRIOR OF THE ORDER: Silver, parcel-gilt. Philipp Jakob VI Drentwett, Augsburg, c.1736–1737.

302 PENDANT MEDALLION: Gold, partly enamelled. German, 18th century.

303 STAR OF THE ORDER OF ST HUBERTUS: Gold, partly enamelled, brilliants and rosettes. Gottfried Merk, Munich, 1868.

Commissioned by King Ludwig II of Bavaria (r. 1864–1886).

INSIGNIA OF ORDER OF THE GOLDEN FLEECE

The Order of the Golden Fleece was founded on 10 January 1430 by Duke Philip the Good of Burgundy on the occasion of his marriage to Isabella of Portugal. Through marriage, the Hapsburgs, in the person of Emperor Maximilian I became Grand Masters of the Order, this position later passing to the Spanish line of the Hapsburg family through Emperor Charles V. When the Spanish line died out, Emperor Leopold I became Grand Master in 1700. After the Spanish War of Succession, Philip V, of the Bourbon ruling house of Spain, proclaimed himself Grand Master. Since that time there have been two branches of the Order of the Golden Fleece in existence: a Spanish and an Austrian Order. The patron saint of the Order is St Andrew; its emblems are the golden ram's fleece of the Jason legend, flint and fire-iron. The device is "Ante ferit quam flamma micet" (He strikes before the spark flies).

The emblem of the Order is called the "toison", the rings of the attachment, the "coulant".

304 COULANT OF THE GOLDEN FLEECE (known as the "SpanishToison"): Brilliants, silver-gilt mount. Probably Spain, towards 1742.

Presented to the Electoral Prince and later Elector Max III Joseph by the French Ambassador, Marshal Belle-Isle, on behalf of the Spanish King, on the occasion of the prince's father's imperial coronation in 1742.

305 TOISON OF THE GOLDEN FLEECE: Brilliants, gold, silver-gilt mount. Munich, c.1750.

306 COULANT OF THE GOLDEN FLEECE: Rubies, brilliants, silver-gilt. Munich, c.1750.

307 COULANT OF THE GOLDEN FLEECE: Brilliants, silver-gilt mount. Munich, c.1750.

308 TOISON OF THE GOLDEN FLEECE: Sapphires, brilliants, gold, silver-gilt. Munich, c.1760.

309 TOISON OF THE GOLDEN FLEECE: Almandine, brilliants, rubies, gold, silver-gilt. German, c.1760–1770.

310 TOISON OF THE GOLDEN FLEECE: Brilliants, gold, silver-gilt, glass. Munich, 1761.

311 TOISON OF THE GOLDEN FLEECE: Brilliants, glass stones, gold, silver-gilt. Munich, 1763.

312 TOISON OF THE GOLDEN FLEECE: Gold, silver-gilt, brilliants. Johann Staff, Munich, 1765.

◁ Cat. 309 Toison of the Golden Fleece, c.1760–1770

313 HAT BROOCH: Brilliants, silver-gilt. Johann Staff, Munich, 1765.

314 CHAIN FOR THE ORDER OF THE GOLDEN FLEECE: Gold, silver-gilt, cold painting. German, probably 18th century.

OTHER ORDER EMBLEMS AND SOUVENIRS

315 MALTESE CROSS: Gold, enamel. German, towards 1799.

Made for Prince Karl of Bavaria (1795–1875) who received the dignity of a Grand Prior of the Order of the Knights of Malta in Germany in 1799.

316 BROOCH OF THE THERESE ORDER: Brilliants, silver-gilt. Munich, 1828; altered by the Munich jeweller Opitz, 1835.

Commissioned by King Ludwig I of Bavaria. The Order of Therese was founded by his consort, Therese of Saxony-Hildburghausen, on 12 December 1827 to support unmarried daughters of the Bavarian nobility.

317 CRAVAT RING: Brilliants, silver-gilt. Probably Munich, c.1830.

318 HAT BROOCH: Brilliants, sapphires, silver-gilt. Gottfried Merk, Munich, 1874.

319 HAT BROOCH: Brilliants, rubies, gold, silver-gilt. Gottfried Merk, Munich, 1875.

The hat brooches (Cat. 318 and 319) were commissioned by King Ludwig II of Bavaria (r. 1864–1886) and were made from gemstones already in the Treasury.

320 PEARL CHAIN: The chain is made from 90 pearls from Bavarian rivers.

CRYSTAL CARVINGS

In the second half of the 16th century, glyptic art advanced beyond the previously practised gem and cameo carving. Pitchers, bowls, cups and table fountains were carved from large rock crystals in so-called crystal mills (grinding mills). Northern Italy, in particular Milan, was the dominant centre of the crystal and gem carving art in the second half of the 16th century. As a result of the emigration of Italian artists, the Prague Court Atelier, founded by Emperor Rudolf II, began to thrive in the first half of the 17th century.

Duke Albrecht V's plan to establish a crystal mill in Munich under the management of one of the Sarachi brothers from Milan failed. More and more orders were placed with the Milanese glyptic artists Fontana and Sarachi, whose crystal carvings therefore also represent the basis of the Munich crystal collection.

The heyday of gem carving came to an end around 1700.

Rock-crystal, like the related dark smoke quartz (mistakenly called smoke topaz), belongs to the quartz group. It was found in the Alps, but most sites have now been exhausted.

321 ROCK-CRYSTAL SHRINE OF DUKE ALBRECHT V: Rock-crystal, ebony, enamelled gold mounts, lapis lazuli, onyx cameos, rubies, emeralds, pearls. Rock-crystal work: Annibale Fontana, Milan, c.1560–1570. Wooden parts: ascribed to Hans Krieger, Augsburg, c.1570. Goldsmith work: ascribed to Ulrich Eberlin, Augsburg, c.1570.

The crystal carvings show scenes from the Old Testament and Greek mythology and have panels with grotesque-style decoration. The crystal shrine was purchased by Duke Albrecht V of Bavaria. Until 1614/1615 it was located in the Treasury vault and was moved into the Rich Chapel on the orders of Maximilian I. Since 1958 it has been back in the Treasury.

322 AMPHORA (known as the "Jason Vase"): Rock-crystal, enamelled gold mount, rubies. Annibale Fontana, Milan, c.1570–1575.

The engraving shows scenes from the legend of Jason.

323 JUG WITH TWO SPOUTS (known as the "Proserpina Jug"): Rock-crystal, enamelled gold mount, rubies, emerald, onyx cameos. Annibale Fontana, Milan, c.1570-1575.

324 TABLE FOUNTAIN: Rock-crystal, enamelled gold mount, onyx cameos. Probably Fontana's workshop, Milan, c.1570–1575.

325 JUG AND COVER: Rock-crystal, enamelled gold mount. Gasparo Miseroni, Milan, c.1570–1575.

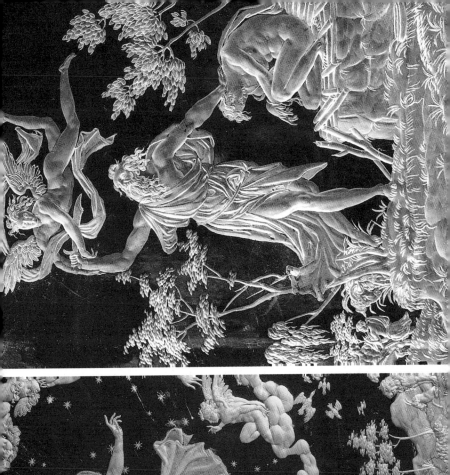

326 VESSEL IN THE FORM OF A SWAN: Rock-crystal, almandine, silver-gilt mount and fire-gilded cast bronze. Milan, c.1570–1575. Mount: after 1779.

On the vessel are depicted scenes from the story of Hippolytus. The original mount was richly decorated with precious stones and cameos.

327 LARGE CUP: Rock-crystal, enamelled gold mount. Circles around the Fontana workshop, Milan, c.1570–1575.

The scenes depict the story of Io.

328 ORNATE VASE (amphora): Rock-crystal, enamelled gold mount, rubies, emeralds. Sarachi brothers or the workshop of Gasparo Miseroni, Milan, towards 1579.

The figural frieze depicts the triumphal carriage and procession of Bacchus, the God of Wine. The vase was delivered to the Bavarian court in 1579, together with the "galley" bowl (Cat. 329).

329 ORNATE BOWL (in the form of a galley): Rock-crystal, silver-gilt mount and fire-gilded cast bronze. Sarachi brothers, Milan, 1579. Mount: after 1779.

The sides of the bowl are engraved with scenes from the Old Testament (the Miracle of Manna and Moses striking water from the rock). In 1779 the mount was so damaged that it was melted down and replaced with a new, simple mount.

330 ORNATE JUG (known as the "Joseph Jug"): Rock-crystal, enamelled gold mount, rubies, spinels, pearls. Sarachi brothers, Milan, c.1570–1580.

The figural frieze encircling the body of the jug depicts two scenes from the Old Testament: Joseph accuses his brothers and Joseph embraces Benjamin and recognises his brothers.

331 ORNATE JUG (known as the "Callisto Jug"): Rock-crystal, enamelled gold mount with pearls and emeralds. Probably the Sarachi workshop, Milan, c.1570–1580.

Figural frieze with scenes from the legend of the nymph Callisto.

◁◁ Cat. 321 Rock-crystal shrine of Duke Albrecht V, A. Fontana, c.1560–1570 and Augsburg, c.1570

◁ Cat. 321 Details of rock-crystal shrine of Duke Albrecht V, A. Fontana, c.1560–1570

Cat. 328 Ornate vase, Milan, towards 1579

332 POURING VESSEL: Rock-crystal, silver-gilt mount. Circles around the Sarachi workshop, Milan, c.1570–1580.

Figural scenes on the sides of the vessel: the Judgement of Paris and the Abduction of Helen.

333 ORNATE BOWL (in the form of a galley): Rock-crystal, silver-gilt and bronze mount. Circles around the Sarachi workshop, Milan, c.1570–1580. Mount: after 1779.

The carved decoration (The Flood and Noah's Ark) is presumably based on engravings which vary a theme of Michelangelo. The original mount, a ship's deck, was melted down in 1779 and replaced by the present one.

334 JUG: Rock-crystal, enamelled gold mount, emerald. The workshop of Gasparo Miseroni, Milan, c.1570–1580.

335 ORNATE BOTTLE: Rock-crystal, enamelled gold mount, rubies, emeralds, diamonds, pearls. Milan, c.1570–1580.

Two oval, carved crystal plates are joined together in the form of a pilgrim's flask. Each of the two crystal sides has a large figural composition: on one side is the drunken Silenus in the midst of dancing maenads and satyrs playing instruments; on the other side is Bacchus, throned on two leopards and surrounded by maenads and satyrs, receiving Apollo who descends from the skies.

336 FOUR-CORNERED BOTTLE: Rock-crystal, enamelled gold mount. Milan, c.1570–1580.

337 TAZZA: Rock-crystal, enamelled gold mount. Milan, c.1570–1580.

338 VASE AND COVER: Rock-crystal, enamelled gold mount set with rubies. Milan, c.1580. Mount: probably South German, c.1650–1660.

The picture frieze shows a Bacchanalian procession in a landscape entwined with vines.

339 JUG AND COVER ("Hunting Jug"): Rock-crystal, enamelled gold mount, glass cover. Probably German, c.1580–1600.

The hunting scene (a pig hunt) is one of the oldest on rock-cut vessels. "A golden rose" originally sat on the knop of the lid.

340 LARGE CUP AND COVER (in the form of a basilisk): Rock-crystal, silver-gilt mount. Probably Milan, c.1580. Mount: renewed in 1779.

Cat. 330 Ornate jug (known as the "Joseph Jug"),
Sarachi brothers, Milan, c.1570–1580   ▷

341 LARGE CUP: Rock-crystal, enamelled gold mount, rubies, pearls. Probably Milan, c.1580-1590. Mount: probably German, late 16th century.

342 TAZZA: Rock-crystal, enamelled gold mount. Probably Milan, c.1580–1590.

343 STANDING CUP: Smoky-quartz, gold mount. Probably Prague, c.1600.

344 SMALL BOWL: Smoky-quartz, silver-gilt and enamelled mount. Probably Dionysio Miseroni, Prague, c.1630.

345 SMALL BOWL: Smoky-quartz, silver-gilt and enamelled mount. Probably Prague, c.1600.

346–347 EWER AND BASIN: Rock-crystal, gold mount, silver-gilt parts, rubies, diamonds. Probably Milan, c.1600.

The ewer and the basin probably came from the bridal dowry of Princess Anna Catharina Constanza, daughter of Sigismund III of Poland; in 1642 she married Philipp Wilhelm, who later became Palatine Elector. In the centre of the basin is the Polish royal coat-of-arms with the initials "SR" (Sigismundus Rex), pointing to King Sigismund III Vasa (r. 1587–1632).

348 CUP AND COVER: Rock-crystal, enamelled gold mount. Probably Freiburg i. Br., c.1600.

349 CUP AND COVER: Rock-crystal, enamelled gold mount, chalcedony. Milan or Prague, c.1600. Knop: Italian, c.1550.

The cover was not an original part of the bowl. The decoration on the head of the bust is set with a ruby; the clasp on the robe is set with a turquoise.

350 SHELL-SHAPED VESSEL: Rock-crystal, smoky quartz. Probably Prague, c.1600.

351–352 EWER AND BASIN: Rock-crystal, silver-gilt mount, enamelled gold ornament, rubies. Probably Freiburg i. Br. or Milan (Miseroni workshop), c.1600–1610.

In the centre of the basin is the coat-of-arms of the Dukes of Württemberg.

353 BOWL: Rock-crystal, enamelled gold mount. Probably Prague, c.1610.

◁ Cat. 322 Amphora (knowns as the "Jason Vase"), detail,
A. Fontana, c.1570–1575

354 CUP: Rock-crystal, silver-gilt mount. Probably Ferdinando Eusebio Miseroni, Prague, c.1677–1678. Mount: probably 18th century.

355 DIPPING VESSEL: Rock-crystal, enamelled gold mount, red-brown glass paste. Probably Polish, c.1610.

356 VESSEL IN THE FORM OF A FABULOUS BEAST: Rock-crystal, silver mount. Probably Prague, c.1610–1620. Mount: probably 18th century.

357 CUP: Rock-crystal, silver-gilt mount. Probably Prague, c.1610–1620. Mount: probably 18th century.

358 SMALL SALVER: Rock-crystal. Probably Prague, c.1610–1620.

359 CUP: Rock-crystal, silver-gilt mount. Probably Prague, c.1610–1620.

360 SMALL RECTANGULAR BOTTLE: Rock-crystal, enamelled gold mount. Probably Prague or Milan, c.1610–1620.

361 SMALL JUG: Rock-crystal, silver-gilt mount. Probably Prague, c.1620.

362 TAZZA: Rock-crystal, silver-gilt mount. Probably Prague, c.1620.

363 TAZZA: Rock-crystal, enamelled gold mount, rubies, diamonds, pearls. Probably Prague, c.1620. Griffin: c.1560–1570.

It is probable that the Griffin was formerly a pendant. Hans Reimer, the Munich goldsmith, is thought to have been the craftsman, perhaps following a design by Hans Mielich.

364 FLACON: Rock-crystal, silver-gilt mount. Probably German, c.1620–1630.

365 SALVER: Rock-crystal. Probably Prague, c.1620-1630.

366 CUP: Rock-crystal, enamelled gold mount. Hans Wilhelm Deck, c.1630.

Resting on a sturdy stem in the form of a lion is a six-sided bowl with scenes from the legend of Io. The landscape frieze around the bowl shows a view of Munich, opposite an ancient columned ruin.

367 TAZZA: Rock-crystal, silver-gilt mount. Probably Prague, c.1630.

368 CUP AND COVER: Rock-crystal, silver-gilt mount. Probably Salzburg, c.1665–1670.

369 LARGE JUG: Rock-crystal, silver-gilt mount. Probably Dionysio and Ferdinando Eusebio Miseroni, Prague, c.1661–1663.

Single hollowed-out rock-crystal monolith, with carved-out handle. The figure of a crouching lion is suggested in the design.

370 ORNATE CUP AND COVER: Rock-crystal, silver-gilt and enamelled mount. Probably Salzburg, c.1670.

371 BEAKER WITH SCREW COVER: Rock-crystal, silver-gilt and enamelled mount, garnets. Perhaps Freiburg i. Br., c.1650.

The figures on the sides of the beaker depict the Creation of Eve and the Fall in the midst of a Paradise-like landscape with animals. The sun, moon and stars are depicted inside the curved cover.

372 GOBLET: Rock-crystal, silver-gilt mount. Perhaps Freiburg i. Br., c.1650–1660.

373 SMALL CUP: Rock-crystal, silver-gilt and enamelled mount. German, c.1670–1680.

374 SMALL BOX: Rock-crystal, gold mount. Perhaps Salzburg, c.1690–1700.

375 SALVER: Rock-crystal, partly gilded bronze. German, c.1710.

THE ART OF CUTTING GEMSTONES

When gem carvings were acquired, not only craftmanship and artistic quality were of decisive importance, but also colour symbolism and gem magic. Still in the spirit of mediaeval tradition, various stones were attributed with the characteristics of certain planets and were believed to have a corresponding apotropous effect.

Amethyst and Chalcedony

Amethyst and chalcedony belong to the quartz group. Traditionally amethyst deposits were found in the Auvergne, Ceylon and India. Martian characteristics were attributed to violet amethyst, and it was used as an amulet to protect against drunkenness. Chalcedony was found in Egypt and Arabia; later deposits were found in Madagascar, Ceylon, Syria, Iceland and Transylvania. Chalcedony was thought to have properties of the God Saturn.

376 CUP: Amethyst, enamelled gold mount. Probably German, first half of 17th century.

377 ORNATE CUP AND COVER: Chalcedony, enamelled gold mount, rubies, pearls, onyx. Probably Sarachi brothers, probably Milan, c.1570.

378 BOWL: Chalcedony, enamelled gold mount. Probably German, c.1600.

379 SMALL CUP: Chalcedony, enamelled gold mount, emeralds, diamonds. Probably German, c.1610–1620.

380 CUP AND COVER: Chalcedony, enamelled gold mount, cameos, agate and carnelian. Probably German, c.1650-1660. Cameos: probably Italian, c.1570.

381 CUP AND COVER: Chalcedony, enamelled gold mount. Probably East German, c.1660–1670.

382 ORNATE CUP AND COVER: Chalcedony, enamelled gold mount, rubies, emeralds, diamonds. Probably German, c.1670.

◁ Cat. 377 Ornate cup and cover, Sarachi brothers, probably Milan, c.1570

383 BEAKER: Chalcedony and agate, enamelled gold mount. Probably German, 17th century. Mount: c.1690–1700.

384 BOWL: Chalcedony. Probably 17th century.

385–386 TWO BOWLS: Chalcedony. Probably 17th century.

387 BOX: Chalcedony, silver mount. German, c.1690–1700.

388 BOWL: Chalcedony, gold mount. Probably French, c.1720.

Agate, Onyx

Agate also belongs to the quartz group. If properly cut, dark agate can produce onyx, which is used to particular artistic effect in cameo carving. The colouring of agate varies at different layers in the stone and this fact was exploited as far back as Graeco-Roman times. Since Roman times there have been highly productive deposits of agate in the vicinity of Idar-Oberstein; Schlottwitz and Halsbach in Saxony as well as Peninsular India also have deposits. Agate was regarded as the Mercurial gem and as an amulet against poisons.

389 HALF-LENGTH FIGURE OF CLEOPATRA: Reddish/yellowish agate, enamelled gold mount. Italian, c.1550. Mount: German, towards 1600 and 1700–1710.

390 CUP AND COVER: Yellow-brown to grey agate, enamelled gold mount. German (probably Nuremberg), c.1560.

391 BUST OF MALE FIGURE: Onyx, enamelled gold mount. Italian, c.1560–1570.

392 BOWL AND COVER: Dark agate (brecciated agate), enamelled gold mount, diamonds. Italian, c. 1570.

393 TAZZA: Onyx (bordering on chalcedony), enamelled gold mount, diamonds, rubies. Milan, c.1570.

394 VASE ("May Jug"): Yellow-brown agate, enamelled gold mount. Italian, (probably Milan), c.1570.

395 BOWL AND COVER: Red to dark brown agate (brecciated agate), enamelled gold mount, rubies, pearls. Italian (probably Milan), c.1570–1580.

Cat. 393 Tazza, Milan, c.1570 ▷

396–399 FOUR CARVED GEMSTONES (intaglios): Agate and onyx, silver-gilt mount. Italian or French, c.1570.

Engravings of Love's Sacrifice, Couple at Altarstone, Callisto the nymph and Hercules.

400 VASE AND COVER: Brown to grey agate, enamelled gold mount. Italian, c.1570–1580.

401 FLACON: Agate, gold. Probably Italian, c.1570–1580.

402–407 SIX VASES ("May Jugs"): Red-brown to yellow agate, gold rubies, pearls, wood. Probably Milan, c.1570–1580.

408 BOWL: Reddish/yellow agate (bordering on chalcedony), enamelled gold mount. Probably Milan, c.1570–1580.

409 CUP AND COVER: Agate, onyx, enamelled gold mount, diamonds, sapphires, emeralds. Probably Milan, c.1580.

410 TAZZA: Agate, partly enamelled gold mount. Probably Prague, c.1590.

411 CUP: Grey-brown to greenish agate (brecciated agate), enamelled gold mount. Italian or Prague, c.1590.

412 SMALL BOTTLE: Agate, enamelled gold mount, diamonds. Italian or Prague, c.1590–1600.

413 CUP AND COVER: Pink to grey-brown agate, enamelled gold mount, pearls. J. Kobenhaupt (?), perhaps Stuttgart, c.1610–1620.

414 CUP AND COVER: Yellow-brown to blue-grey agate (brecciated agate), enamelled gold mount. Probably Prague c.1590–1600.

415–416 TWO PENDANTS with bust portraits of Christ and Mary: Agate, chalcedony, lapis lazuli, garnets, enamelled gold mount. Ottavio Miseroni, Prague, c.1590–1600.

417 RELIEF with bust portrait of Christ: Agate. Probably Ottavio Miseroni, Prague (or Italy), c.1600.

418–419 KNIFE AND FORK: Yellow-brown to red-brown agate, silver-gilt, steel. Italian or German, c.1600.

420 TAZZA: Red-brown to grey agate, silver-gilt mount. German c.1610–1620.

421   TAZZA: Yellow-brown agate, silver-gilt and enamelled mount. Probably Prague, c.1610–1620.

422   TAZZA: Yellow-brown agate, silver-gilt and enamelled mount. Probably Prague, c.1620–1630.

423   PENDANT: Red-brown agate, silver-gilt mount. Italian, c.1640–1650.

424   SMALL CUP: Agate, enamelled and silver-gilt mount. Probably German, early 17th century.

425–428   TWO CREDENCES, TWO CUPS AND COVERS: Red-brown agate, silver-gilt filigree, emeralds. Probably Italian, c.1650.

429   MEDALLION PENDANT (head of Minerva): Onyx, enamelled gold mount, amethysts. German, c.1650.

430–431   TWO CANDLESTICKS: Red to yellow-brown agate, silver-gilt mount. Master's mark "BH", Frankfurt a. Main, c.1660–1670.

432   HERM: Agate, garnet, topazes, opals, peridot, pearls. German, c.1660–1670. Head: Italian, 15th century.

433   HERM: Agate, peridot, citrine, pearls. German, c.1660–1670. Head: probably French, 14th century.

434   HERM: Agate, smoky-quartz, citrine, turquoises, pearls. German, c.1660–1670. Head: Italian, c.1570.

435   HERM: Agate, chalcedony, citrine, garnets, turquoises, pearls, silver-gilt. German, probably 1660–1670. Head: probably French, 13th/14th century.

436   SMALL CUP: Grey agate, rose quartz, silver-gilt mount. German, c.1670.

437   ORNATE CUP ("Eagle Bowl"): Brown agate, gold and silver-gilt mount, enamel, rubies, diamonds. German, c.1690–1700. Gem carving and eagle: probably c.1600–1610.

438–441   KNIFE, FORK, SPOON, SALT CELLAR: Yellow-brown to violet agate, silver-gilt mount, steel, turquoises. German, c.1690–1700.

442   OVAL BOWL: Red-brown, yellow flecked agate. Probably 17th century.

443   OVAL BOX: Agate mosaic (pietra dura). Probably 17th century.

444   SMALL BOX WITH LID: Dark brown agate. Probably 17th century.

445–446   TWO SMALL BOXES WITH SLIDING LIDS: Agate mosaic (pietra dura). Probably 17th century.

447   CUP AND COVER: Brown to grey agate (possibly chalcedony), enamelled gold mount and silver-gilt mount, lapis lazuli, onyx. German, towards 1700. Knop figure: Italian, c.1570–1580.

448   TAZZA: Red-brown agate, silver-gilt mount, precious stones. Mount: Michael I Heckel, Augsburg, c.1690.

449–451   CUP AND TWO SPICE PLATES: Red-brown agate, enamelled gold mount. German, towards 1700.

452   SMALL CUP AND COVER: Brown agate, enamelled gold mount, ruby. German or French, c.1700–1710.

453–454   TWO CANDLESTICKS: Yellow-grey agate. German, c.1700–1720.

455   BUST OF BACCHUS in baroque mount: Grey-brown agate, silver-gilt mount. Gem carving: Giacomo Anfosso (?), Italian (probably Rome), c.1560–1580. Mount: German, c.1710-1720.

456   LARGE TAZZA: Yellow-brown and reddish agate, enamelled gold mount. German, 1723.

457   BOX: Yellow to grey agate (brecciated agate), gold mount. German, towards 1740.

458   KNIFE: Red to violet agate, steel. 17th to 18th centuries.

Heliotrope, also called blood jasper, is a close relative of chalcedony. Its characteristic is the brilliant red of iron oxides embedded in deep green. In the Middle Ages it was believed to have special magical properties, as the red was thought to be drops of Christ's blood. The principal source of heliotrope is India (Kathiawar Peninsula). It was regarded as a solar gem with the magic properties of the "invisible".

459   CUP: Heliotrope. Gasparo Miseroni, Milan, 1556.

The cup is most probably the one presented by Giorgio Vasari in 1556 as the main work of the master stone-cutter Gasparo Miseroni of Milan.

460   BOWL AND COVER: Heliotrope, enamelled gold mount, diamonds, rubies. Milan, c.1570.

461   BOWL: Heliotrope. Milan, c.1570.

462   BOWL: Heliotrope, enamelled gold mount. Italian, c.1570–1580.

463   SMALL CUP: Heliotrope, enamelled gold mount, diamonds, rubies, pearls. Italian or Prague, c.1590.

464   TAZZA : Heliotrope, enamelled gold mount. Italian or Prague, c.1590.

465   TAZZA: Heliotrope, enamelled gold mount. Italian or Prague, c.1590–1600.

466   BOWL: Heliotrope, enamelled gold mount, diamonds, rubies. Probably Prague, c.1590–1600.

467 SHALLOW VESSEL: Heliotrope, enamelled gold mount. Workshop of Johann Kobenhaupt, Stuttgart, c.1610–1620.

468   BOWL AND COVER: Heliotrope, enamelled gold mount. Perhaps Salzburg (or Prague), c.1600.

469   TABLE CLOCK: Heliotrope, enamelled gold mount, garnets. Probably Prague, c.1600.

470   BEAKER: Heliotrope, silver-gilt mount. Probably Prague, c.1600.

471–474   FOUR CANDLESTICKS: Heliotrope, red to green agate, silver mount. German, towards 1650.

475 CUP: Heliotrope, silver-gilt mount, pearls. Gem carving: probably Prague, c.1650–1660. Mount: Johann Eissler, Nuremberg, c.1680.

476 OVAL SALVER: Heliotrope, silver-gilt and mostly enamelled mount. Peter Winter, Augsburg, c. 1670–1680.

477 CUP AND COVER: Heliotrope, enamelled gold mount, onyx, rock-crystal, rubies. Paris, c.1670.

Jasper

Like heliotrope, chalcedony, agate, etc., jasper is a mineral of the quartz group. Dominant colours are yellow, reddish brown or green. Egypt has the most well known deposits of jasper, which is also called hornstone. Martian properties were attributed to jasper.

478 BOWL: Green jasper, enamelled gold mount. Milan, c.1560.

479 CUP AND COVER: Yellow-brown jasper, enamelled gold mount, diamonds, rubies, emeralds, jacinth, pearls. Italian, c.1570. Head of knop figure: probably French, 14th–15th centuries.

Acquired by Duke Albrecht V of Bavaria.

480–481 EWER AND BASIN: Red-brown to gold-yellow jasper, enamelled gold mount, diamonds, pearls. Ewer: probably Sarachi brothers, Milan, c.1570–1580. Basin: perhaps Prague, c.1620.

482 CUP: Yellow jasper, enamelled gold mount. Probably Milan, c.1570–1580.

483 CUP AND COVER: Yellow jasper, enamelled gold mount, onyx cameos, rubies, emerald, pearl. Probably Italian, c.1580.

484 BOWL: Red jasper, enamelled gold mount. Probably Italian, c.1580.

485 LARGE CUP: Yellow jasper, enamelled gold mount, rubies, pearls. Probably Italian, c.1580–1590.

486 SMALL BOWL WITH OWL: Green jasper, enamelled gold mount. Probably Italian, c.1590–1600.

487 CUP: Yellow jasper, red agate, enamelled gold mount. Workshop of Johann Kobenhaupt, Stuttgart, c.1610–1620.

488 SMALL SQUARE BOTTLE: Brown jasper, enamelled gold mount. Probably Prague, c.1610 – 1620.

489 GOBLET: Red jasper, silver-gilt mount. Probably German, c.1630.

490 SHALLOW VESSEL: Red jasper. Probably German, c.1650.

491 CUP: Red-brown jasper, silver-gilt mount. Probably German, c.1660.

Aventurine

A stone of the quartz group, usually dark green with metallic shimmer from inclusions of fuchsite. The more common yellowish brown or red aventurine obtains its colour from inclusions of iron oxide platelets.

492 SMALL BOWL: Green aventurine, c.1600.

Nephrite

Nephrite belongs to the jade group. The principal colour is green. The most important deposits are found in China. Because it is a very hard stone, nephrite has been in demand since prehistoric times for use in making weapons and tools; for this reason is is also called axestone.

493 BOWL: Nephrite, silver-gilt mount. Probably Italian, c.1580 – 1590.

494 BOWL: Dark green nephrite, enamelled gold mount. Italian or Prague, c.1600 – 1610.

495 – 499 FIVE SMALL CONTAINERS: Mid-green nephrite, silver-gilt mount. Probably German, c.1610 – 1620.

500 BOWL: Pale green nephrite, enamelled gold mount, garnets. Probably Prague, c.1620.

501 CUP: Mid-green nephrite, silver-gilt and enamelled mount. Probably Prague, c.1650.

502 CREDENCE: Nephrite, enamelled gold mount. Probably French or German, c.1700 – 1710.

Serpentine

The "snake-coloured" greenish or yellowish mineral is well suited for turning on the lathe, because of its low hardness.

503 SMALL BOWL: Serpentine, silver-gilt mount. Probably 17th century.

Lapis Lazuli

Inclusions of iron pyrites appear in the deep, strong blue of the stone as glittering granules on the surface and enhance the colour attraction. Deposits used to be found in Afghanistan and the quarries at Lake Baikal. The magical qualities of Venus were attributed to lapis lazuli.

504 BOWL: Lapis lazuli, gold mount: Probably Milan, c.1570–1580.

505 BOWL: Lapis lazuli, enamelled gold mount. Italian or Prague, c.1590.

506–507 EWER AND BASIN: Lapis lazuli, enamelled gold mount, silver-gilt mount, emerald, rubies, diamonds. Probably Milan, c.1590.

Acquired by Duke Albrecht V of Bavaria.

508 SMALL JUG: Lapis lazuli, enamelled gold mount, set with rubies, diamonds and pearls. Probably Prague, c.1590.

On the sides of the jug are three carved lapis lazuli intaglios with representations of Diana with hunting hounds, Orpheus playing a musical instrument and the horned Actaeon. The knop figure, Eros with bow, was added in the 18th century.

509–510 TWO JARS: Lapis lazuli, enamelled gold mount. Probably Prague, c.1600.

511 TAZZA: Lapis lazuli, gold mount, diamonds. Probably German, c.1650–1660.

512 SCREW-TOP JAR: Lapis lazuli, silver-gilt, enamel. Nikolaus Fischer, Augsburg. c.1652.

513–515 BOX AND TWO TRAYS: Lapis lazuli, silver-gilt, partly enamelled, pearls. Probably Augsburg, c.1670.

516 TOBACCO BOX: Lapis lazuli, gold mount. Probably Pierre Jean Briceau, Paris, c.1760.

Garnet

Red garnet, also called carbuncle, occurs only in relatively small crystals and is therefore not suitable for making large vessels. More frequently used is pyrope, from Bohemia, west of Trebnitz. Garnet from Asia Minor is often called almandine, after its place of discover (Alabanta). The main deposits are found in Ceylon (Sri Lanka). The magic powers of the sun were attributed to garnet and it was used as an amulet against fever and plague.

517   SMALL BOWL: Garnet, enamelled gold mount. Probably German, c.1600.

518   SMALL BOWL: Garnet. Probably German, c.1670-1690.

Pietra Dura

Inlay work with variously coloured precious stones first appeared in Italy in the late 16th century; during the first half of the 17th century this technique increased in popularity. The name (pietra dura means hard stone) distinguishes it from inlay work in coloured stucco marble (scagliola).

519   STATE TABLE: Hans Georg Hertel, after a design by Lucas Kilian, Augsburg, 1626. Pietra dura top: probably Cosimo Castrucci, Prague, c.1580.

Inlay work in precious stones (agate, jasper, lapis lazuli), ebony, pearwood, walnut, rare woods; gold, gold enamel, silver, tin and bronze.
In the middle of the table top, a large, octagonal landscape picture in pietra dura technique. The surrounding silver, bronze and tin inlays depict lions with the Bavarian and Lorrainese coats-of-arms, representations of the four seasons, the four elements and emblems between ornamental tendrils. Close to the shorter sides of the table is the monogram of Maximilian I and his first consort, Elisabeth of Lorraine.

ROOM VIII

HIGH AND LATE RENAISSANCE

Interest in the natural world fostered by humanism and the discovery of strange lands gave rise to a preference for curiosities and unusual materials from all over the world. Materials such as ivory, amber, rhinoceros horn, coconut and ostrich egg shells, coral and narwhal tusks were particularly favoured. In the ducal collections of art and natural history (Kunst- und Wunderkammern) these items were assembled, often artistically shaped into cups, table centrepieces and the like. Enamel work enjoyed great popularity. From the beginning of the 17th century, artistic compositions of organic materials and precious mountings retreated more and more in favour of articles made of silver, gold and precious stones.

Initially, Nuremberg was the foremost city in Germany for goldsmithing, but from the end of the 16th century it was superseded by Augsburg. In addition, from the middle of the 16th century, Munich ateliers made their appearance also with outstanding works, most of which were for the ducal courts.

Amber

Since prehistoric times amber, a fossilized tree resin, has been traded and used in artistic works. The largest deposits in Europe were found along the East Prussian coast. Several different types of amber were used, often in combination with each other for artistic effect.

520 CUP AND COVER: Amber. Workshop of Stenzel Schmidt (?), Königsberg, c.1570–1580.

The four small medallions between the lions heads show portraits of Duke Albrecht of Prussia (r. 1525–1568), his wife Anna Maria of Brunswick, his son, Albrecht Friedrich (r. 1568–1618) and his son's wife, Maria Eleonore of Jülich-Cleve-Berg.

521 WRITING BOX: Amber. Workshop of Stenzel Schmidt (?), Königsberg, c.1570–1580.

On the lid, male and female profile picture in costumes of the period (the heraldic eagle with "S" on the breast probably refers to King Sigismund III of Poland); on the front, bust of Christ and Mary; on the other sides, five unidentified busts.

◁ Cat. 614 Table bell, Wenzel Jamnitzer,
Nuremberg, c.1560–1570

522 TAZZA AND COVER: Amber, ivory. Königsberg, 1590.

The coat-of-arms probably refers to Sigismund III, the first King of Poland from the House of Vasa.

523 TANKARD: Amber, silver-gilt mount. Königsberg, c.1600.

524 TANKARD: Amber, painting on glass (églomisé), enamelled gold mount. Georg Schreiber (?), Königsberg, c.1640.

525 SMALL BOX: Amber, wood. Georg Schreiber (?), Königsberg, c.1640.

526–527 KNIFE AND FORK: Amber. Danzig or Elbing, c.1650.

528–529 TWO TANKARDS: Amber, silver-gilt mount. Probably Jakob Heise, Konigsberg, c.1660.

530–531 TWO PIN-BOXES: Amber. Probably East Prussia, 17th/18th centuries.

532 TOBACCO BOX: Amber. Stolp (?), c.1710.

533 TOBACCO BOX: Amber. North German, c.1720.

From the estate of the Empress Amalia, daughter of Emperor Joseph I, and consort of Elector Carl Albrecht (1742–1745 as Emperor Karl VII).

Mother-of-Pearl, Rhinoceros Horn, Coconut, Coral, Bezoar etc.

534 BOWL: Mother-of-pearl. German (Königsberg?), c.1550.

535 CUP AND COVER: Rhinoceros horn. Cover and mount: gold, enamel. German (Vienna?), c.1590.

A rhinoceros (after a woodcut by Albrecht Dürer, 1515) is depicted on the cover; on the inside of the cover, an Austrian escutcheon with the letters "CE-ZO" ("Carl Erzherzog von Österreich" – Carl, Archduke of Austria). After the death of the Archduke (1618) the cup and the Duchy of Jülich-Berg passed to Pfalz-Neuburg, through the Archduke's wife, Sybille, daughter of Duke Wilhelm of Jülich.

536 CUP AND COVER: Rhinoceros horn, enamelled gold mount. German, c.1600.

537 BOWL: Madrepore, silver-gilt mount. Mount: German, c.1620. Bowl: perhaps East Asian.

538 CUP: Madrepore, enamelled gold mount. German (Prague?), c.1620.

539 CUP: Coconut, silver-gilt mount. German, 17th century.

540 CUP: Coconut, silver filigree mount. German or Italian, late 17th century.

541–544 FOUR CUPS: Coconut (?), silver-gilt mount. German, 17th century.

545–549 WRITING BOX: Ivory, gold, "émail sur verre". German, c.1620.

In the box an inkpot and sandbox; accessories are scissors, two penknives and a writing pen. The rare "émail sur verre" technique involves inlaying fine gold sheet into a design engraved on coloured glass plates, and then applying translucent enamel colour.

550 BOWL ORNAMENTED WITH SHELL-WORK: Silver-gilt, partly enamelled in colour. Johann Baptist I Weinold, Augsburg, c.1635–1640.

The shell-work in the bowl depicts four allegories of Virtue, surrounded by thirteen oval medallions with portraits of emperors from the House of Hapsburg. On the base, representations of the four continents.

551 AMULET: Coral, enamelled gold mount. Italian, c.1600.

The ends of the coral branch are carved, two in the form of fists (with the thumb between the first two fingers), as a protection against the Evil Eye.

552 AMULET: Coral, silver-gilt mount. 17th century.

553 AMULET: Coral, gold mount. 17th century.

Cat. 552 and 553 are from the estate of the Empress Amalia, daughter of Emperor Joseph I, and consort of Elector Carl Albrecht (1742–1745 as Emperor Karl VII).

554 BEZOAR STONE: Enamelled gold mount, emeralds. German, c.1570-1580.

Bezoar stones (a hard mass which forms in the stomachs and intestines of certain breeds of goat or sheep) were particularly prized for their supposed healing powers, and as an antidote to poisons.

555 BEZOAR STONE: Enamelled gold mount. German, c.1600.

556 BEZOAR STONE: Silver-gilt mount. German, c.1610–1620.

557   BEZOAR STONE: Silver-gilt mount. German, c.1650.

558   BEZOAR STONE: Silver-gilt and enamelled mount. German, c.1650.

The Art of the Goldsmith

Many of the works from the centres of the art of goldsmithing in the 16th and 17th centuries which are now kept in the Treasury are linked with the names of the most important master craftsmen of the time: Wenzel and Hans Jamnitzer, Hans Lencker and Hans Karl in Nuremberg, Johannes Lencker and Matthäus Walbaum in Augsburg and Hans Reimer in Munich. Also exhibited are works by other German and European workshops. The objects were partly commissioned by the Bavarian dukes, and partly brought to the Treasury as dowries or gifts from other ruling houses.

559   CUP: Silver-gilt, narwhal bone insets, ostrich egg on dome. Nuremberg, c.1550. Cover: 1593.

On the knop a lion holds the coat-of-arms with the monogram of Duke Philipp Ludwig of Pfalz-Neuburg.

560   STAFF OF DUKE ALBRECHT V OF BAVARIA: Ivory, gold, enamel, cameos. Ascribed to the workshop of Abraham I Lotter or Ulrich Eberlin, Augsburg, c.1570–1575.

561   CUP AND COVER: Gold, enamel. Ascribed to Hans Reimer, Munich, 1562.

The blue and white walls of the cup bear three coats-of-arms (Bavaria, Austria and the Alliance) in scrollwork cartouches. On the knop a standing lion bearing the Bavarian shield with the letters "A.H.I.B." (= "Albrecht Herzog in Bayern") and the date "1562". The Austrian coat-of-arms refers to the consort of Albrecht V, Anna, daughter of Emperor Ferdinand I.

562   ORNATE CUP (known as the "Sapphire Cup"): Gold, enamel, sapphires. Hans Reimer, Munich, 1563.

The cup was made for Duke Albrecht V of Bavaria, perhaps to designs by Hans Mielich. The whole cup is coated with white enamel set with 36 large sapphires. The gold base shows through as slender vine tendrils in the uncoated areas.

563   TANKARD: Gold, partly enamelled, diamonds, emeralds, pearls, narwhal bone insets. Hans Reimer, Munich, 1572.

The narwhal bone insets show relief scenes from the Life and the Passion of Christ. On the inside of the cover is the Bavarian coat-of-arms; on the base a representation of the Last Supper. Made for Duke Albrecht V of Bavaria.

Cat. 563 Tankard, Hans Reimer,
Munich, 1572   ▷

564 RAPIER: Hilt and girdle: Gold, enamel. Blade: steel damascened with gold. Hilt and sheath: South German (Nuremberg?), 1571. Blade: Spanish, c.1550.

565 JEWEL CASKET WITH TRAY INSERT: Silver-gilt, diamonds, rubies, emeralds, heliotrope. Wenzel Jamnitzer, Nuremberg, c.1550–1560.

On the sides, gold reliefs of the Labours of Hercules. In the central niches on the front and rear walls, statuettes of Opulentia (Riches) and Custodia (Watchfulness). In the velvet-lined interior is a tray insert with two drawers.

566 CUP AND COVER: Jasper, silver-gilt mount. Bowl: probably Italian. Mount: Wenzel Jamnitzer, Nuremberg, c.1560–1570.

567 ORNAMENTAL JUG: Mother-of-pearl spiral shells, silver-gilt mount, partly enamelled. Wenzel Jamnitzer, Nuremberg, c.1570.

568–569 EWER AND BASIN: Copper, enamel paintings. Mount: bronze and silver-gilt. Pierre Reymond and Leonhard Limosin, Limoges, c.1562. Mount: ascribed to Wenzel Jamnitzer.

Scenes depicted on the jug are the Gathering of Manna and Moses striking water from the rock. Also depicted on the basin is the Gathering of Manna and the four Evangelists in oval sections on the rim.

570 CREDENCE: Copper, enamel painting. Monogrammist "J.C." (probably Jean de Court), Limoges, c.1570.

The grisaille painting represents Poseidon and Amphitrite.

571 CREDENCE: Copper, enamel painting. In the style of Martial Courteys, Limoges, c.1570.

The grisaille painting represents the Choice of Hercules.

572 CUP AND COVER: Silver-gilt. Antwerp, 1557–1558. Cover: Gillis Sibricht, Cologne, before 1587.

On the walls of the cup, the Procession of Poseidon and Amphitrite with retinue and fantastic sea creatures.

573–574 EWER AND BASIN: Silver-gilt, partly enamelled, turquoises. Hans II Schweinberger, Augsburg, c.1580–1590.

Around the base of the basin a frieze relief (fighting Tritons, sea-centaurs and fabulous creatures, with Galatea and Poseidon).

Cat. 573 Ewer, Augsburg, c.1580–1590 ▷

575 ORNATE CUP: Silver-gilt, enamel. Cornelius Gross, Augsburg, c.1560–1570.

576 ORNATE CUP: Silver-gilt. Lukas I Schaller, Augsburg, c.1570–1580.

577–578 TWO STANDS: Silver, enamel. Hans Lencker, Nuremberg, c.1580.

579–583 WRITING BOX: Silver, parcel-gilt, enamel. Hans and Elias Lencker, Nuremberg, c.1580.

On the corners of the lower section of the box, four putti with the attributes of Grammar, Mathematics, Astronomy, and Music, crowning the lid the figure of Rhetorika. On the walls and lid surfaces hunting scenes in a forest landscape with grotesques. Remaining accessories for the box are a ruler marked in different measuring units, a small and a large pair of scissors, and a small knife.

584 DRINKING VESSEL (in the form of a stag): Silver-gilt. Elias Zorer, Augsburg, c.1586–1590.

The head of the stag is removable; inside the neck is a gilt cup.

585 CUP: Silver, partly enamelled, niello. Elias Zorer, Augsburg, c.1590–1595.

586–587 WRITING BOX: Silver, parcel-gilt. Matthäus Walbaum, Augsburg, c.1594.

588 DIANA WITH STAG (drinking game): Silver, repoussé, parcel-gilt. Matthäus Walbaum (or circles around him), Augsburg, c.1600.

Unlike similar "drinking games" there are no traces of wheels or a clockwork mechanism. Normally these table pieces, filled with wine, would travel along the table-top and come to rest in front of one of the guests, who would then drink the contents.

589–590 TWO HAND BASINS: Silver-gilt. Ascribed to Andreas Attemstett and Cornelius Erb, Augsburg, c.1585–1590.

Repoussé and chased multifigural reliefs on the base (The Fall of the Giants, Deucalion Flood); on the rim allegories of the four elements and the four seasons.

591 CUP AND COVER: Rock-crystal, enamelled gold mount, rubies, emeralds. Ascribed to Ulrich Eberlin, probably Augsburg, c.1580–1590.

592 THE RADZIWIL BOWL: Gold, partly enamelled, rubies, diamonds, emeralds. Ascribed to Hans Karl, Nuremberg or Salzburg, after 1600.

The coat-of-arms and inscription on the base refer to Prince Janusz VII Radziwill, who in 1600 received the title of Duke of Sluzk and "Pocillator Ducatus Lithuaniae".

593 BOWL: Gold, enamel, emeralds, rubies, sapphires, narwhal tusk. Probably made by King Sigismund III of Poland himself, c.1600.

In the curve of the bowl between the narwhal bone insets are the coats-of-arms of Poland, Sweden, Lithuania and the House of Vasa.

594–595 TWO ORNAMENTAL VASES: Silver, parcel-gilt, amethyst insets. German, c.1600.

596–597 CUP AND CREDENCE PLATE: Nautilus shell, silver-gilt mount. Bohemia (?), c.1600.

598 CUP (known as the "Electoral Cup"): Gold, partly enamelled. Vienna or Prague, 1620.

On the cover, a statuette of Emperor Matthias; on the bowl, the seven Electors. On the stem, statuettes of Spes, Fides and Caritas (Hope, Faith and Charity); the inscription on the cover refers to the election and coronation of the Emperor.

599 CUP AND COVER: Silver-gilt. Dutch (?), c.1520 or 1640.

Frieze relief, the "Battle of the Wild Men"; on the vase-shaped knop, a statuette of Judith.

600 CREDENCE: Silver-gilt, partly enamelled. German, c.1600.

601–602 EWER AND BASIN: Silver-gilt, Italian or German, c.1620.

On the ewer, reliefs of scenes from the life of Pompey; on the basin, scenes from the life of Caesar. Cat. 559, 600, 601 and 602 are from the estate of the daughter of Sigismund III of Poland, Anna Catharina Constanza, who married to Philipp Wilhelm of the Palatinate in 1642.

603 CUP IN THE FORM OF A SHIP: Fossilized palm wood, silver-gilt mount, enamel, diamonds, rubies. Johannes I Lencker, Augsburg, c.1611–1614.

The Latin inscription on the rim of the bowl reads: "I was once a palm tree, then began to fossilize and am now a skiff. If Neptune is not my ferryman, then it shall be Bacchus." On the "stern" of the ship-shaped bowl is Triton with the electoral coat-of-arms of Bavaria. The goldsmith's signature is below the head of the dolphin on the base.

604 CUP (known as the "Marburg University Cup"): Silver, parcel-gilt. Artist's monogramm "NB", Frankfurt (?), c.1630.

This is a copy of the cup made by Master Paul Birkenholz for the jubilee of Marburg University in 1627.

605 SALVER: Silver-gilt, mother-of-pearl. Hans III Petrus, Augsburg, c.1635–1640.

606 NAUTILUS CUP: Nautilus shell, silver-gilt mount, partly enamelled. Düsseldorf, towards 1660.

607 CUP: Mother-of-pearl spiral shell, silver-gilt mount. Nuremberg, c.1660.

Smaller Works

608 GOLD RELIEF (Adam and Eve): Gold, ivory, silver, lapis lazuli. German (Nuremberg?), c.1550. Frame: early 17th century.

After copper engravings by Albrecht Dürer of Adam and Eve and St Eustace.

609–612 TOY BOX: Silver, gold, partly enamelled, rubies, diamonds, emeralds, pearls, ivory. German, c.1560–1570.

Accessories to the box are three huntsman's whistles (deer and roedeer).

613 CHAIN: Gold, enamel, diamonds. Munich (?), c.1560-1570.

614 TABLE BELL: Silver. Wenzel Jamnitzer, Nuremberg, c.1560–1570.

615 BASKET AND COVER: Silver. Ascribed to Hans Jamnitzer, Nuremberg, 1575.

Silver plaquette depicting the Judgment of Paris against a detailed landscape background; the figures are modelled on an engraving by Marcantonio Raimondi which goes back to Raphael.

616 SMALL FLAGON: Agate, enamelled gold mount, diamonds, rubies. Circles around the Jamnitzer workshop, Nuremberg (?), c.1560–1570.

617 BEAR AS HUNTSMAN: Silver-gilt, coated with ambergris, diamonds, rubies, pearls. Hans II Ment, Augsburg, c.1570–1575.

Under the removable head is a silver-gilt cup.

618 HAND-BELL: Silver, parcel gilt, painting on glass (églomisé). German, 1571 (?).

619–620 TWO SMALL GLOBES (terrestrial and celestial): Ivory, gold, enamel. Mount: Nuremberg (?), c.1570–1580.

◁ Cat. 603 Cup, J. I. Lencker, Augsburg, c.1611–1614

621 CHAIN: Gold, enamel, diamonds, garnet, rubies, pearls. German, c.1570–1580.

622 LION AS SUPPORTER OF COAT-OF-ARMS: Gold, enamel, baroque pearl. Paris, towards 1698.

The lion belongs to the clock (Cat. 729); the two have been displayed together since 1995 in Room IX.

623 ST GEORGE (statuette): Gold, enamel, diamonds, heliotrope. German, c.1570–1580. Socle: early 17th century.

624 BUST OF A TURK: Gold, enamel, sapphire. Munich, c.1580. Head: Italian, c.1520.

This is the cover knop of a crystal vessel which has not survived.

625 FIGURE OF A DRAGON: Gold, partly enamelled, rock-crystal, silver-gilt mount, diamonds, rubies. German, c.1580–1590. Mount of base: second half of 17th century.

The dragon was the handle of a crystal vase which went missing after 1783.

626 SALT CELLAR: Gold, enamel, diamonds, rubies. Poland, c.1590.

627 TOP OF A SALT CELLAR: Gold, enamel, diamonds, rubies. Poland, c.1590.

628 SNUFFERS: Silver-gilt. Friedrich Hillebrand, Nuremberg, c.1590–1600.

629 BRUSH: Silver-gilt mount. Augsburg, c.1600.

630 HOUR-GLASS: Silver, parcel-gilt, glass. Boas Ulrich, Augsburg, c.1595–1600.

631 BROOCH: Gold, enamel, diamonds, pearls. Hans Georg Beuerl (jeweller), Augsburg, 1603.

In the form of a trophy. On a painting of the Duchess Elisabeth of Lorraine, the first consort of Elector Maximilian I (Munich, Bavarian National Museum, Engelhard de Pee?, c.1610), the brooch is worn on her left upper sleeve.

632 CASE: Silver, parcel-gilt. Abraham Zeggin, Munich, 1604.

Case for the brooch Cat. 631.

Cat. 606 Nautilus cup, Düsseldorf, towards 1660 ▷

633 INCENSE CONTAINER: Silver-gilt. German (Augsburg?), c.1620.

634 HAND-BELL ("Weather Bell"): Gold, emeralds, pearls. German (?), 17th century.

Pendants

635 PENDANT: Gold, partly enamelled, diamonds, rubies, pearls. German, c.1550–1560.

On three thin chains hangs the figure of a bear coated with ambergris. On top of the bear is a monkey. The pendant is from the estate of the Electoral Prince Joseph, who died in 1699, son of Elector Max Emanuel.

636 PENDANT (Elephant): Gold, enamel, ruby spinel, diamonds, baroque pearl. Probably Hans Reimer, Munich, 1555–1559.

The elephant pendant is depicted on a portrait of Duchess Anna, wife of Duke Albrecht V of Bavaria, which can be found as a miniature by Hans Mielich 1557/1559 in motets by Cipriano de Rore (Munich, Bavarian State Library). Compared to the painting later changes to the pendant become obvious (e.g. baroque pearl instead of the original diamonds).

637 PENDANT: Gold, enamel, aquamarine. Ascribed to a workshop from circles around Abraham I Lotter, Augsburg, c. 1560. Design: perhaps Hans Mielich.

According to the instructions of Albrecht V (1565) the upper mount originally held a diamond (now aquamarine), the lower mount a ruby (now doublet) and a pearl pendant (not preserved).

638 PENDANT: Gold, enamel, diamonds, rock-crystal. Probably Hans Reimer, Munich, towards 1565.

The ruby described in the instructions of Albrecht V (1565) was later replaced by a rock-crystal and the original ruby transferred to a toison of the Order of the Golden Fleece (Cat. 309). The pendant appears on a 1643 portrait by Joachim Sandrart of the Archduchess Maria Anna of Austria, the second consort of Elector Maximilian I of Bavaria (Ambras Castle near Innsbruck).

639–640 TWO PENDANTS (heart-shaped lockets): Gold, enamel. Ascribed to Ulrich Eberlin, Augsburg, c.1560–1565.

641 PENDANT with parrot: Gold, enamel, emeralds, rubies, baroque pearl. Circles around the workshop of Abraham I Lotter, Augsburg, c.1590. Parrot: probably Spanish.

Cat. 649 Watch on ring, probably Augsburg, c.1580 ▷

642 PENDANT ("Cleopatra"): Gold, enamel, jacinth, diamonds, rubies, emeralds. Gem carving: Italian, c.1550. Mount: German, c.1590.

643 PENDANT (known as the "Palatine Lion"): Gold, partly enamelled, diamonds, rubies, emeralds, pearls. German, c.1570–1580.

644 TRIANGULAR PENDANT: Gold, enamel, diamonds. Munich (?), c.1600.

From the estate of Elisabeth of Lorraine, the first consort of Elector Maximilian I of Bavaria. The large triangular diamond in the middle was replaced after 1640 by six small diamonds on a grid-like mount.

645–646 TWO EARRINGS: Gold, diamonds. German, 17th century.

Rings, Watches, Cutlery

647 RING: Gold, enamel, rubies, diamonds. Augsburg or Munich, c.1560–1570.

The ring case opens up to reveal depictions of the Annunciation, Two Shepherds and the Birth of Christ.

648 RING: Gold, enamel, emerald. Munich (?), c.1570–1580.

649 WATCH ON RING: Gold, enamel. Probably Augsburg, c.1580. Watchmaker: probably Jakob Wittmann, Augsburg.

In the lid, two fold-out sections inscribed with IHS monogram of Christ, and inside the Crucifixion and the Instruments of Passion.

650 RING: Gold, sapphire. German (?), 16th century.

651 RING: Gold, partly enamelled, diamonds, emerald. German, c.1650.

652 RING: Gold, partly enamelled, diamonds. German, c.1650.

653 POCKET WATCH: Silver. Augsburg, c.1620. Watchmaker: Conradt Rerizer.

On the folding lid and base, engravings of the Adoration of the Magi and the Resurrection. Five dials for the hours, quarter hours, days, months and phases of the moon.

654 PENDANT WATCH WITH CHIMES: Copper-gilt, silver. Lyon, c.1620. Watchmaker: Jean Vallier.

On the lid and base engravings of the Annunciation and Birth of Christ.

655 PENDANT WATCH AND WRITING IMPLEMENTS: Copper-gilt, rock-crystal, silver-gilt. German, c.1620–1630.

Screwed to the pendant watch is a set of tubular writing implements which can be taken apart. Inscribed on the implements are multiplication tables and a monthly calendar with sliding indicator.

656 POCKET WATCH: Copper-gilt. Ulm, c.1650. Watchmaker: Johann Sayller.

Dial with hours, months and position of the sun in the zodiac.

657 ST GEORGE SPOON: Silver-gilt. Friedrich Hillebrandt, Nuremberg, c.1590.

The handle of the spoon unscrews to reveal a thin quill case with fold-out bone marrow extractor and toothpick; the removable spoon head is attached to a two-pronged fork.

658–663 TWO CUTLERY SETS: Gold, partly enamelled, rubies, diamonds. German, c.1650.

664 SPOON: Silver-gilt. Breslau, c.1620.

665 SPOON: Gold, partly enamelled. Munich, 1639.

The spoon comes from the inventory of the Silver Treasury of the Munich Residence, which was removed for safety to escape the Swedish siege of Munich in 1648. However, the ship transporting it on the river Inn sank near Mühldorf. The spoon was found in 1851 by a fisherman from Neuötting.

666–667 KNIFE AND FORK: Gold, enamel, diamonds. German, towards 1650.

Cat. 727 Table clock, Augsburg, c.1680

BAROQUE, ROCOCO, CLASSICISM

In the 17th and 18th centuries, the Augsburg goldsmith craft experienced its greatest development and gained an international reputation. Augsburg goldsmiths were commissioned by the Prussian Court as well as Swedish, Danish and Russian clients. In contrast to the representative, ceremonial objects of the high and late Renaissance, commissions were now becoming more frequent for articles to serve the personal use of the ruler. Many of the objects in this room came to Munich in 1777 and 1799/1800 along with the Palatine Treasure.

Goldsmith's Work

668 SCREW-TOP CONTAINER: Silver-gilt, agate, red glass pastes. Johann Baptist I Weinold, Augsburg, c.1645–1650.

669 SCREW-TOP BOTTLE: Silver-gilt, enamel, agate. Marx Merzenbach, Augsburg, c.1680.

670–675 FIVE SMALL BOTTLES AND A BOX: Gilded and enamelled copper, corals. Italian, second half of 17th century.

676 DISPLAY DISH: Silver, parcel-gilt. A member of the Jäger family, Augsburg, c.1665–1670.

Depicted on the dish is a silver repoussé relief of Roman soldiers hunting stags and lions.

677 SMALL BOTTLE: Silver-gilt. Friedrich I Schwestermüller, Augsburg, c.1684–1689.

678–679 TWO VASES: Silver-gilt, enamel, precious stones. German (Augsburg ?), c.1680–1690.

680–681 TWO CACHEPOTS (flower-pots): Silver-gilt, enamel, precious stones. German, c.1680–1690.

682 ORNATE SALVER: Silver-gilt, enamel paintings, precious stones. Anton Grill, Augsburg, c.1680–1685. Relief: Johann Adreas Thelott. Enamel paintings: probably Augsburg, end of 17th century.

In the centre of the salver, silver repoussé relief of the Gods in Olympia; on the rim round medallions with enamel paintings of Perseus freeing Andromeda, Diana and Endymion, Athene and the Nine Muses, Venus and Apollo, Venus and Adonis and Pyramis and Thisbe.

683   DISPLAY DISH: Silver, repoussé. Jacob I Warnberger, Augsburg, c.1689.

In the centre of the dish relief of "Pomona and Vertumnus".

684–685   TWO WATER BOTTLES: Silver-gilt, enamel, rock-crystal. German, c.1680–1690.

686   JUG ("May Jug"): Silver-gilt, enamel, precious stones. South German, (Augsburg ?), c.1690.

687   ORNATE SALVER: Silver, parcel-gilt, precious stones and pastes. Johann I Mitnacht and Johann Andreas Thelott (relief), Augsburg, c.1686.

In the centre of the salver silver repoussé relief of the Glorification of the Good Regiment.

688   SALVER: Silver-gilt, precious stones. South German (Augsburg?), late 17th century. Cameos: probably North Italian, 16th and 17th centuries.

689–690   BUSTS OF MARS AND BELLONA: Silver, parcel-gilt, precious stones and decorative stones. Busts: Christoph II Drentwett. Flower bushes: Johann III Beckert. Augsburg, c.1680–1685.

The busts decorated with tall flower bushes were first mentioned in the inventory of the Mannheim treasury in 1733. In 1794 they came to Munich and in 1806 were placed in the Rich Chapel of the Residence. After 1889 the flower bushes were separated from the busts; since 1958 the busts have been on display in the Treasury. In 1994 it was possible to reunite them with the flower bushes which had been believed to be lost.

691–692   TWO FLOWER BASKETS: Silver-gilt, silver filigree, turquoises, amethysts, peridots, garnets, topazes. German, c.1700.

693   VASE: Silver-gilt, silver filigree. German, c.1700.

694   HUNTING KNIFE, BELT AND SHEATH: Nephrite, silver, gold, enamel, diamonds. French, towards 1710.

695–696   TWO ORNAMENTAL SHIELDS: Silver, parcel-gilt, enamel paintings. Johann Georg Sigmund Kohler, Augsburg, c.1695-1700. Reliefs: Johann Andreas Thelott. Medallions: probably contemporary Augsburg works.

On the rim of each shield twelve medallions with portraits of Roman emperors and empresses; in the centre silver repoussé reliefs (Victoria, Tiber [the river god], Romulus and Remus with the she-wolf, equestrian statue of a Roman emperor, Roma [town goddess], and Neptune).

697–698 TWO SMALL BASKETS: Silver-gilt, turquoises. German c.1710–1720.

699–700 TWO ORNAMENTAL PLAQUES: Silver, parcel-gilt. Frame: Johann Christoph I Drentwett. Reliefs: Johann Andreas Thelott. Augsburg, c.1722–1726.

701–702 TWO SWORD HILTS: Silver-gilt, brilliants, emeralds. Daniel Gouers (Govaers), Paris, c.1720–1730.

Cat. 702, after a design by Juste Aurèle Meissonnier. A gift from King Louis XV of France to the Bavarian Elector.

703 WRITING SET: Silver-gilt. Bernhard Heinrich Weyhe, Augsburg 1745-1747.

704 DRINKING HORN MOUNTED AS A DOLPHIN: Bull's horn, silver. Mount: Joseph Anton Seethaler, Augsburg 1797–1799.

The horn, which was originally used as a drinking horn, was converted into a reliquary in St Emmeram Monastery in Regensburg in 1361. Several mounts are recorded. The last and current mount dates from 1797/1799. In 1811 the horn passed as a secularisation acquisition (without the relics) to the Rich Chapel in the Munich Residence.

Caskets

705 CASKET: Silver-gilt, precious stones, copper. Nikolaus Fischer, Augsburg, c.1652. Reliefs: South German, first half of 17th century.

Eight repoussé reliefs in copper-gilt depict scenes from the Passion.

706 JEWEL CASKET: Silver, parcel-gilt and enamelled, precious stones. South German (Augsburg?), c.1660–1670. Cameos: only some are contemporary works.

707 JEWEL CASKET: Silver-gilt, rock-crystal, precious stones. South German (Augsburg?), c.1660–1670. Carved gems and cameos: probably North Italian, c.1600.

Rock-crystal engravings with hunting landscapes and allegorical putti scenes.

708 JEWEL CASKET: Silver-gilt, enamel, precious stones. Balthasar Gelb, Augsburg, c.1695–1700.

709 TRINKET BOX: Silver-gilt, copper, precious stones. South German (Augsburg?), c.1670–1680. Cameos and coral-work: Italian, second half of 17th century.

710 CASKET: Silver-gilt, precious stones. Augsburg, c.1690.

711–716 CASKET FOR JETTONS: Tortoiseshell, silver-gilt, precious stones. German, c.1690.

The casket contains two small trays, two small boxes and 75 jettons of tortoiseshell, mother-of-pearl and cedar wood. (See Cat. 812/813 for description of matching candlesticks).

717 JEWEL CASKET: Enamelled silver-gilt, precious stones. Johann Heinrich Mannlich, Augsburg, late 17th century. Cameos: North Italian, 16th and 17th centuries.

The knop on the lid is a seated Minerva with shield, helmet and spear; in the base a repoussé relief of Athene and the Seven Arts.

718 JEWEL CASKET: Silver-gilt, rock-crystal, precious stones, enamel. Jonas Laminit, Augsburg, c.1665–1670.

Rock-crystal insets with engraved allegories of the four elements and the four seasons.

719 CASKET: Copper-gilt, precious stones. German, c.1710–1720.

720 CASKET: Tortoiseshell, agate, gold, mother-of-pearl. German, c.1725.

Clocks, Calendars, Measuring Instruments

721–722 TWO SAND-GLASSES: Silver, glass. Italian (Venice?), 17th century.

723 CALENDAR CLOCK: Silver-gilt, enamel, precious stones. Augsburg, c.1660. Works: Nikolaus Rugendas.

724 PLATE CLOCK: Silver-gilt, enamel, precious stones. Augsburg, c.1660.

725 PLATE CLOCK: Silver-gilt, enamel, precious stones. South German (Augsburg?), c.1660–1670.

Below the dial, an aspersorium with rock-crystal lid; above, an oval medallion with miniature painting of The Baptism of Christ.

726 MUSICAL CLOCK: Silver-gilt, enamel, precious stones. Case: Heinrich Mannlich, Augsburg, c.1670–1675.

On the top, a revolving, cast silver putto with garland of laurel leaves pointing at the hour with a palm branch. Below the dial, a silver repoussé relief of Atalanta's Race. Inside, a musical clockwork mechanism.

727 TABLE CLOCK: Silver-gilt, enamel, carved shells, cameos, precious stones. Augsburg, c.1680. Works: signed "LAS".

The shell carvings on the slope of the top show portraits of the emperors from the House of Hapsburg. Top of lid: double-headed imperial eagle.

728 SAND-GLASS: Silver, glass. German (?), c.1680–1690.

729 PENDULUM CLOCK: Silver, parcel-gilt and partly enamelled, precious stones. Probably Josias Belle, Paris, towards 1698. Works: probably Henri Martinot.

On the base panel, the monogram of Elector Max Emanuel; below the dial, a gold relief depicting a battle from Max Emanuel's Turkish War (the crossing of the River Save, 1688). The lion (Cat. 622) is mentioned in a bill dated 8.10.1698, from the Parisian jeweller and art dealer, Lorenz Danet, as the crowning piece for the clock. In the 1745 inventory of the Treasury of the Munich Residence the lion is also mentioned in connection with the clock. In 1931 the lion was removed; in 1995 it was replaced.

730 TABLE CLOCK: Silver, parcel-gilt and partly enamelled, tortoiseshell, mother-of-pearl, precious stones, wood. Augsburg, c.1710–1720. Works: Johann Wilebrand.

731–736 CASE WITH DIAMOND SCALES : Gold. German (?), first half of 18th century.

The case contains the scales, a pincette, a small spoon, a needle and various weights.

737–743 CASE WITH INSTRUMENTS: Silver-gilt, chagrin leather, steel. Jakob Boser, Vienna, c.1725.

The case contains a folding knife with horn handle, a pair of scissors, a pair of dividers, a ruler, a pencil case and a needle with spoon-shaped end.

744 CALENDAR TABLET: Silver, parcel-gilt. Frame: probably Johann Christoph I Drentwett. Relief: Johann Andreas Thelott, Augsburg, c.1722.

The revolving discs show the phases of the moon, the days of the month, the names of the months, the saint's days and the signs of the zodiac as well as the hours of day and night of the current month. The central relief shows the start of a hunt.

745 CALENDAR: Gold, enamel. French, c.1755.

Inside the container is a French calendar for 1758.

Cups, Tablewares

746 NAUTILUS CUP: Nautilus shell, silver-gilt, enamel, wood, precious stones. Nuremberg, c.1660–1670.

747 SPOON: Gold, enamel, diamonds. South German or Vienna, c.1680.

748 – 750 KNIFE, FORK AND SPOON: Gold, enamel, precious stones, steel. Augsburg, c.1680 – 1690.

751 OYSTER SHELL: Silver-gilt. German (probably Augsburg or Neuburg on the Danube), 1691.

The inscription states that the oyster shell was found in 1691 in the stomach of a deer bagged by the Palatine Count Philipp Wilhelm August the Younger. The shell was subsequently fitted with a precious mount.

752 – 775 TEA SERVICE: Silver-gilt, enamel paintings. Johann Georg Sigmund Kohler, Augsburg, c.1705. Enamel painting: as yet unknown Augsburg master.

The enamel paintings (landscapes, still-life flowers and strewn flowers, scenes from mythology and Roman history) are modelled on Italian and French monumental painting from the second half of the 17th century.

776 BOWL: Mother-of-pearl, silver. France (probably Paris), c.1710 – 1720.

777 HUNTING CUP: Silver-gilt. Nikolaus Ulrich Heckel, Augsburg, c.1712 – 1715.

The boar's tusk bent as ring is supported on a stem encircled with boars heads. It was given as a gift to Elector Max Emanuel of Bavaria in 1711.

778 – 795 DINNER SERVICE OF EMPRESS MARIA AMALIA: Silver-gilt. Johann Erhard II Heuglin, Augsburg, c.1722 – 1726.

All pieces have engraved Regency ornamentation and cast medallions with allegorical figures. From the estate of Empress Maria Amalia, daughter of Emperor Joseph I, and consort of Elector Carl Albrecht of Bavaria (1742 – 1745 as Emperor Karl VII). Probably belonged to the toilet set, Cat. 815 – 827.

796 CUP: Rock-crystal, silver-gilt, enamel, precious stones. South German or Vienna, c.1725.

797 – 800 KNIFE, FORK, SPOON, EGG-SPOON: Gold, enamel, steel. Augsburg (?), c.1725.

Cat. 815 – 827 Container from a toilet set, Augsburg and Berlin, c.1725 – 1730 ▷

801 DRINKING VESSEL (in the form of a stag): Silver, parcel-gilt. Johann Engelbrecht, Augsburg, c.1731.

In the neck of the animal is a silver beaker. According to the inscription engraved on the collar, Elector Carl Albrecht himself shot the stag in 1731; incorporated in the hunting trophy is a piece of the antlers carved to represent their original form.

802 HUNTING CUP: Silver-gilt. Josef Ignatz Volkom(b), Munich, towards 1740.

On the stem of the cup, a withered stag's antlers found in 1738 in the Elector's pheasant garden near Nymphenburg Palace.

803 HUNTING CUP: Silver-gilt, enamel. Johann Jakob Adam, Augsburg 1753–1755.

The two tusks encircling the cup come from a large wild boar bagged by Elector Max III Joseph himself in 1753.

804 CHOCOLATE CREDENCE: Silver-gilt, glass, porcelain. Johann Jakob Adam, Augsburg, c.1765–1767. Porcelain cup: Frankenthal, c.1765.

805–809 CUTLERY SET (Knife, fork, spoon, salt cellar and toothpick): Gold, enamel, steel. Augsburg, late 17th century.

Toilet Pieces and Sets

810–811 TWO CANDLESTICKS: Agate, silver-gilt. German, c.1680–1690.

812–813 TWO CANDLESTICKS: Tortoiseshell, silver-gilt, diamonds. South German or Vienna, c.1680–1690.

Belongs to Cat. 711–716.

814 MIRROR ON STAND: Silver-gilt, precious stones, pearls. German, late 17th century.

815–827 TOILET SET: Silver-gilt, enamel. Johann Erhard II Heuglin, Augsburg, c.1725–1730. Pierre Fromery, Berlin, c.1725–1730.

The technique known as "émail de Saxe" (enamel painting with gold inlays) goes back to Raimund Faltz (1658–1703), a medallionist from Berlin, and his successor, Fromery. Probably belongs to the dinner service Cat. 778–795; as Cat. 828–847 also from the estate of the Empress Maria Amalia.

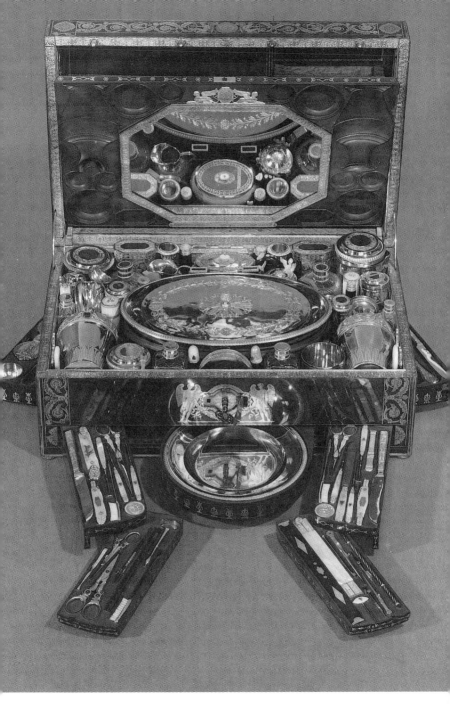

Cat. 939–1061 Travelling set of Empress Marie Louise, M.-G. Biennais, Paris, 1810

828–847 TOILET SET: Silver-gilt, lapis lazuli, precious stones, ivory. Cosimo II Merlini, Florentine court workshops under Giovanni Battista Foggini, probably 1720s.

Made for Maria Amalia, consort of Elector Carl Albrecht of Bavaria (1742–1745 as Emperor Karl VII).

Combined Sets

848–938 LARGE COMBINED SET: Silver-gilt, agate, chalcedony. Matthäus II Baur and Tobias Baur, Augsburg, c.1690–1695 and 1700–1705.

The large set includes table-plates, toilet pieces, writing equipment.

939–1061 TRAVELLING SET OF EMPRESS MARIE LOUISE: Silver-gilt, gold, mother-of-pearl, tortoiseshell and other materials. Martin-Guillaume Biennais and workshop, Paris, 1810.

The travelling set was presented as a gift by the City of Paris to the second consort of Napoleon, on the occasion of her marriage on 2 April 1810. After the collapse of the Napoleonic Empire the service was transferred to Parma in 1816, as part of the private belongings of the Empress. In 1847 it was inherited by Duke Franz of Modena, from whose estate it transferred to the last Bavarian Queen, Marie Therese and her son, Crown Prince Rupprecht of Bavaria. In 1959 the Bavarian state authorities acquired the service and handed it over to the Treasury.

Boxes

1062 TOBACCO BOX: Mother-of-pearl, gold. Carving: German., c.1650. Mount: c.1750–1760.

On the hinged lid, a relief showing the "Adoration of the Child".

1063–1067 FOUR SMALL ORNAMENTAL URNS AND A BOX: Silver-gilt, turquoises. German, second half of 17th century.

1068 SMALL BOX: Silver-gilt, precious stones. German, second half of 17th century.

1069 SMALL BOX: Silver-gilt, precious stones. German, second half of 17th century.

Cat. 1079 Powder flask, R. de Cuizy, Paris, 1726–1730 ▷

1070–1071 TWO BOXES WITH LIDS: Silver-gilt, enamel, precious stones. German (Augsburg?), c.1680–1690.

1072 SMALL BOX: Gold, silver-gilt filigree. German, c.1700.

1073 BOX: Silver-gilt, precious stones. Augsburg, c.1700. Relief: possibly Johann Andreas Thelott, Augsburg, from the same time.

The relief shows Juno with Peacock and Nymph.

1074 TOBACCO BOX: Tortoiseshell, gold. Perhaps Rémy de Cuizy, Paris, c.1720.

1075 TOBACCO BOX: Enamelled gold, Columbian emerald, glass. Daniel Gouers (Govaers), Paris, 1723–1724.

1076–1077 TWO TOBACCO BOXES: Tortoiseshell, gold. Probably Rémy de Cuizy, Paris, c.1725.

1078 TOBACCO BOX: Gold, chalcedony. French (probably Paris), c.1720–1730.

1079 POWDER FLASK: Gold, enamel, tortoiseshell. Rémy de Cuizy, Paris 1726–1730.

The flask probably comes from the hunting equipment of Elector Max Emanuel.

1080 BOX: Gold, mother-of-pearl, enamel. French, first half of 18th century.

Attached to the inside of the lid is a small gold spoon.

1081–1082 TWO COSMETIC BOXES: Silver-gilt, chalcedony. Florentine court workshops under Giovanni Battista Foggini, probably 1720s.

Belongs to Cat. 828–847.

1083 TOBACCO BOX: Gold, mother-of-pearl, lacquer painting. French (?), c.1750.

1084 TOBACCO BOX: Silver-gilt, fossilized wood. German, c.1760.

1085 BOX: Gold, mother-of-pearl. Paris, c.1765.

1086 TOBACCO BOX: Gold, precious stones. Paris (?), c.1780.

1087   TOBACCO BOX: Gold, enamel. Pierre-François Drais, Paris, c.1785.

The 26 medallions with enamel painting show portraits of the Wittelsbach princes; in the centre of the lid, Elector Karl Theodor of Bavaria (r. 1777–1799).

Statuettes

1088   KNIFE GRINDER: Gold, enamel, precious stones, ivory, tortoiseshell, steel, glass. Ivory carving: German, c.1670–1680. Goldsmith's work: German, c.1700.

The knife grinder is of ivory; on the statuette and the coloured enamel gold cart are diamonds and rubies; the grinding stones are of glass.

1089   GROTESQUE FIGURE OF AN INNKEEPER: Silver-gilt and enamelled silver, diamonds, pearls. Figure: perhaps Ferbecq, German (Frankfurt?), c.1690. Base: Philipp Jakob VI Drentwett, Augsburg, c.1720.

1090   GROUP OF MONKEYS: Silver-gilt, mother-of-pearl, alabaster, precious stones, agate, glass. German (perhaps Saxon), c.1700.

1091   PALATINE ELECTOR JOHANN WILHELM AS MARS: Silver-gilt and enamelled silver, precious stones, pearls. German (Augsburg?), 1704.

1092   STATUETTE OF MINERVA: Silver, parcel-gilt, tortoiseshell, precious stones, ivory, enamel painting. South German (Augsburg?), c.1710. Medallions: probably Augsburg, from the same time.

1093   STATUETTE OF CLEOPATRA: Silver, parcel-gilt, tortoiseshell, precious stones. South German (Augsburg?), c.1710.

1094   STATUETTE OF ABUNDANTIA: Silver, parcel-gilt, enamel, tortoiseshell, precious stones, enamel painting. South German (Augsburg?), c.1710. Medallion: probably Augsburg, from the same time.

1095   STATUETTE OF MERCURY: Silver, parcel-gilt, tortoiseshell, precious stones, enamel painting. South German (Augsburg?), c.1710. Medallion: probably Augsburg, from the same time.

1096   STATUETTE OF VENUS: Silver, parcel-gilt, tortoiseshell, precious stones, ivory, enamel painting. South German (Augsburg?), c.1710. Medallion: probably Augsburg, from the same time.

1097 STATUETTE OF HERCULES: Silver, parcel-gilt, tortoiseshell, precious stones, ivory, enamel painting. South German (Augsburg?), c.1710. Medallion: probably Augsburg, from the same time.

1098 STATUETTE: Silver, parcel-gilt, tortoiseshell, precious stones, enamel painting. South German (Augsburg?), c.1710. Medallions: probably Augsburg, from the same time.

1099 HUNTSMAN AND DOG: Gold, enamel, precious stones, pearls, mother-of-pearl. German (Vienna?), c.1720.

1100 COLOMBINE: Silver-gilt and enamel, precious stones, baroque pearl. Figure: German, c.1720. Pedestal: Daniel Würtz, Strasbourg, c.1730.

1101–1102 TWO STATUETTES OF NEGROES: Ivory, copper-gilt, pearls, precious stones. German, c.1725.

1103–1104 TWO OSTRICHES: Ivory, copper-gilt, precious stones, pearls. German, c.1725.

Smaller Works

1105 PAIR OF SUGAR-TONGS IN THE FORM OF A STORK: Silver. German, 17th/18th centuries.

Such sugar-tongs were popular christening gifts; they are sometimes referred to as "Stork" or "Umbilical" scissors.

1106 "TABULA JOVIS": Gold. German, second half of 17th century.

Probably a sign of membership to a secret circle in the form of a small book.

1107 BEZOAR STONE: Silver-gilt. German, second half of 17th century.

Exhibited in Room VIII; see Cat. 554–558.

1108 SMALL NOTEBOOK: Silver-gilt, enamelled silver, precious stones, tortoiseshell, ivory. Augsburg, c.1680–1690.

1109 CHILD'S RATTLE: Silver-gilt, enamelled silver, diamonds. South German or Vienna, c.1669.

The child's rattle came from the estate of the Hapsburger Maria Antonia, the first consort of the Bavarian Elector Max Emanuel. After her early death in 1692 the rattle came into the possession of her son, Electoral Prince Joseph Ferdinand of Bavaria, who died in 1699 – only 7 years after his mother. The rattle with the badger's claw, which had apotropaic significance, is depicted on a portrait of the Archduchess Maria Antonia of Austria as a child, painted by Gérard du Château, c.1670 (Munich, Bavarian National Museum).

1110 EAU-DE-LA-REINE FLACON: Silver-gilt, garnet, precious stones. Late 17th century.

1111 SMALL LANTERN: Parcel-gilt, precious stones. German, towards 1700.

From the estate of Crown Prince Ferdinand, son of Elector Max Emanuel of Bavaria.

1112–1114 THREE PIN-BOXES: Gold, ivory. German (Vienna?), c.1700.

In the form of figures from the Commedia dell'arte (Harlequins, Mezzetino); from the dowry of Therese Kunigunde, second consort of Elector Max Emanuel of Bavaria.

1115 SMALL VASE: Agate, silver, diamonds. c.1700.

1116 SMALL VASE: Onyx, silver, diamonds. c.1700.

1117 EAU-DE-LA-REINE FLACON : Agate, silver-gilt, diamonds. c.1700.

1118 SMALL NOTEBOOK: Silver-gilt filigree work, ivory. German, c.1700.

1119 CHESSBOARD AND FIGURES: Tortoiseshell, mother-of-pearl, silver-gilt and enamelled silver, diamond chips. South German or Vienna, c.1710.

From the estate of Empress Maria Amalia, consort of the Bavarian Elector Karl Albrecht (1742–1745 as Emperor Karl VII).

1120 PERFUME CAPSULE of Empress Maria Amalia: Gold, enamel, diamonds. Vienna, c.1710.

On the screw-top lid the monogramm "WAJ" with imperial crown, which refers to Emperor Joseph I and his consort, Wilhelmine Amalie of Brunswick-Lüneburg, the parents of Empress Maria Amalia, consort of Elector Carl Albrecht of Bavaria (1742–1745 as Emperor Karl VII).

1121 SMALL DISH with putto: Silver-gilt, agate, coral. German, c.1710–1720. Mount: probably Augsburg.

Evidently the putto originally belonged to Cat. 152.

1122   SMALL NOTEBOOK: Ivory, gold, diamonds, leather. French, c.1710.

Inside are two French calendar sheets from the year 1702 and sheets of notepaper.

1123   FLACON: Gold, enamel, diamonds. German (Vienna?), c.1710–1720.

As Cat. 1120, from the estate of Empress Maria Amalia.

1124   SMALL SPINNING-WHEEL : Silver, lacquer painting, wood. Munich, c.1720. Lacquer painting: German, from the same time.

1125   SPOOL STAND: Silver, lacquer painting, wood. Munich, c.1720. Lacquer painting: German, from the same time.

1126   SMALL NOTEBOOK with pen: Chagrin leather, gold. French, c.1720.

Inside is a French calendar from the year 1723 and sheets of notepaper.

1127   PAIR OF SCISSORS with case: Gold, steel. German, c.1720.

1128   SMALL CHEST: Fossilized wood, copper-gilt, agate. German c.1720–1730.

1129   WALKING-STICK: Gold, precious stones, cane. German (Munich?), c.1730.

1130   WALKING-STICK: Whale-barb, tortoiseshell, gold, mother-of-pearl. German, c.1730.

The stick is a whalebone drilled through at the upper end. It belonged to Duke Karl August of Pfalz-Zweibrücken and after his death (1795) it passed to the Bavarian Lord Steward of the Household, Graf von und zu Sandizell, and finally to King Maximilian II of Bavaria.

1131   KNOB OF CANE: Amethyst, gold, diamonds. French (?), c.1730.

Belonged to Elector Max III Joseph of Bavaria.

1132   KNOB OF CANE: Glass, c.1740–1750.

1133   BALSAM LOCKET: Agate, gold, enamel. South German, c.1750.

Inscription: "Votre amitié en retour"; from the estate of Empress Josepha, daughter of Elector Carl Albrecht of Bavaria, and consort of Emperor Joseph II.

1134   WRITING UTENSILS (stand, ink pot, sand-box, quill knife, 2 seals): Chalcedony, gold. French (?), c.1750.

1135   KNOB OF CANE with miniature watch: Heliotrope, silver-gilt, precious stones, porcelain. German, c.1750 ("WR" monogram). Works: Charles Cabrier the Elder, London, c.1700.

1136   PAIR OF SCISSORS: Gold, steel. French (?), c.1750.

1137   FAN: Mother-of-pearl, gold, diamonds, parchment. French, c.1750. Painting: Lasellon (?).

On the front: coastal landscape and Venus with Amor and the Three Graces visiting Vulcan's smithy.

1138   TOBACCO BOX: Horn, gold. German, c.1760.

1139   UTENSIL FOR CUTTING QUILLS: Brass, iron. J. A. Schnetter, Munich, c.1820–1830.

Jewellery

1140   MEDALLION: Gold, enamel, almandines. Probably Augsburg, c.1760.

From the estate of Empress Maria Amalia, consort of Elector Carl Albrecht (1742–1745 as Emperor Karl VII).

1141   PENDANT in the form of a trophy: Silver, parcel-gilt, enamelled, pearls, precious stones. German (Augsburg?), c.1680.

1142   BROOCH in the form of a butterfly: Diamonds, silver-gilt. German, 18th century.

Belonged to Empress Elisabeth Augusta, the first consort of Elector Karl Theodor of Bavaria.

1143   PENDANT: Gold, enamel, silver, jasper, diamonds. German, 18th century. Cameo with portrait of woman: probably Prague, first half of 17th century.

As Cat. 1140, from the estate of Empress Maria Amalia.

1144   BREAST ORNAMENT: Pear-shaped pearls, diamonds, silver-gilt. German, c.1710–1720.

1145–1148   JEWELLERY FRAGMENTS: Pearls, diamonds, silver-gilt. German, c.1710–1720.

1149 BLACK-AND-WHITE PEARL: (known as the "Palatine Pearl"): Mount: Caspar Mayr, Munich, 1784.

The pearl (called "La perle Palatine", also the "Pfälzisches Aug", i.e. Eye of the Palatinate) was owned by Palatine Elector Johann Wilhelm, who presumably bought it in Amsterdam. The pearl is a unicum. The dark base and the light body of the pearl form an organic unity, i.e. the pearl base cannot have been coloured or inserted at a later point. The present mount was commissioned by Elector Karl Theodor of Bavaria.

1150 RING: Silver-gilt, turquoise. German, c.1670–1680.

1151 RING: Silver-gilt, diamonds, doublets. German, c.1720.

Seals

1152 SEAL: Gold, enamel, sapphire, brilliants. South German or Vienna, c.1690.

Marshalled coats-of-arms of Bavaria and Austria, with electoral cap.

1153 SEAL: Rock-crystal, silver, diamonds, c.1700.

1154 SEAL: Chalcedony, silver-gilt, 18th century.

Carving: Head of Minerva.

1155 SEAL: Garnet, silver-gilt. German, 18th century.

Coat-of-arms of the Electorate of Bavaria, with the inscription "MARIA".

1156 SEAL: Garnet, brilliants, rubies, emeralds, gold, enamel. German, first half of 18th century.

Bavarian coat-of-arms with electoral cap, surrounded by the Chain of the Order of the Golden Fleece and of the Order of the Knights of St George.

1157 SEAL: Jasper, carnelian, diamonds, ruby, silver. German (Vienna?), c.1710–1720.

Crowned monogram APW; coat-of-arms with eagle and crown; crowned column with laurel and inscription "RECTE CONSTANTER" (upright and steadfast).

1158 SEAL: Carnelian, silver-gilt. German, c.1720–1730.

Cupid with bow and dog; inscription "LA FIDÉLITÉ ME MÈNE".

1159 SEAL: Carnelian, silver-gilt. German, c.1720–1730.

Coat-of-arms of the Electorate of Bavaria and Chain of the Order of the Knights of St George.

Cat. 1164 Flagon. Ivory carving: probably Dutch, c.1640. Mount:
Andreas I Wickert, Augsburg, c.1645

1160 SEAL: Rock-crystal, steel. German, towards 1750.

Bavarian coat-of-arms with Chain of the Order of the Golden Fleece; monogram MJ (Elector Max III Joseph of Bavaria); imperial orb in laurel wreath.

1161 SEAL: Rock-crystal, steel. German, towards 1760.

Bavarian coat-of-arms (twice); monogram MEJ (Elector Max III Joseph of Bavaria); all three representations with Chain of the Order of the Golden Fleece.

1162 SEAL: Rock-crystal, silver-gilt. South German, towards 1760.

Bavarian coat-of-arms with electoral cap; monogram JMA (Josepha Maria Antonia, daughter of Elector Carl Albrecht of Bavaria, and consort of Emperor Joseph II) with electoral cap, sunflower and sun with circular inscription "JE NE REGARDE QUE LE SOLEIL".

1163 SEAL: Rock-crystal, silver-gilt. German, c.1760.

Bavarian coat-of-arms with electoral cap, pierced heart, encircled by arrows and circular inscription "UNE SEULE ME PLESSE". Two hands hold lover's knots above a veduta (Vienna?) and circular inscription "EN S'ÉLOIGNANT ELLES SE RESERRENT".

Ivories, Narwhal tusk, Tortoiseshell

1164 FLAGON: Ivory, silver-gilt. Ivory carving: probably Dutch, c.1640. Mount: Andreas I Wickert, Augsburg, c.1645.

Raised relief on sides: Poseidon and Amphitrite in a shell pulled by two Tritons and Amphitrite on a dolphin with three putti and a Nereid.

1165 TANKARD: Ivory, silver-gilt. Ivory carving: German, c.1660–1670. Mount: Tobias Ludwig Krug, Strasbourg, 1761.

Raised relief on the sides: Battle between the Christians and the Turks.

1166 TANKARD: Narwhal tusk, silver-gilt, precious stones. Mount: Marx Merzenbach, Augsburg, c.1670–1680.

1167 TANKARD: Ivory, silver-gilt. Ivory carving: South German (Weilheim or Munich), c.1680. Mount: Weilheim or Landshut.

Raised relief on sides: Fights between lions and bears with dogs and bulls against a woodland landscape with city silhouette.

1168 POWDER FLASK: Ivory, gold, enamel, precious stones. Ivory carving: South German, c.1680–1690. Mount and enamel work: Augsburg, c.1690.

Ivory carvings: stag, boar and fox hunted by hounds. Enamel painting: Endymion preparing for the chase.

1169 LARGE DISH: Silver, parcel-gilt, ivory. Ivory carving: South German, c.1690. Mount: Augsburg, from the same time.

The ivory reliefs show mythological scenes: Venus and Adonis (in centre); Jupiter in the form of Diana with Callisto, Dido invites Aeneas to the hunt, Meleager and Atalante, Vertumnus in the guise of an old woman tempting Pomona (around the outside).

1170 TANKARD: Ivory, silver-gilt. Ivory carving and mount: South German (Augsburg?), c.1700.

Raised relief on the sides: Tritons, sea-nymphs, putti and sea creatures. On the lid: sea monster and putto with arrow riding on a dolphin.

1171–1172 VIOLIN AND BOW: Tortoiseshell. Copy of an Italian model, c. 1700. Bow: kingwood, 17th century.

Rhinoceros and Ibex Horn

1173 ORNATE CUP AND COVER: Rhinoceros horn, silver-gilt, enamel, precious stones. Carving: South German under Dutch influence, c.1660. Mount: German (Augsburg?), from the same time.

Two raised reliefs on the sides of the vessel: Neptune and Amphitrite with sea gods, putti and seahorses.

1174 ORNATE CUP AND COVER: Rhinoceros horn, silver-gilt. Carving: South German, c.1660–1670. Mount: Christoph Leipzig, Augsburg, c.1670.

Raised reliefs on the hull-shaped cup: rhinoceros hunt and cannibals eating.

1175 DRINKING HORN: Rhinoceros horn, silver, enamel, precious stones. Carving: South German under Dutch influence, c.1660–1670. Mount: Augsburg, from the same time.

1176 ORNATE CUP AND COVER: Rhinoceros horn, silver-gilt. Carving: South German, c.1670–1680. Mount: Elias Adam, Augsburg, c.1705.

Raised reliefs on the boat-shaped body of the vessel: natives drinking and eating.

1177 CUP: Rhinoceros horn, silver-gilt. Carving: South German, c.1670–1680. Mount: probably Hans Ludwig Kienle the Younger, Ulm.

Raised relief on the walls of the cup: fight between a rhinoceros and an elephant.

1178 TABLE FOUNTAIN: Rhinoceros horn, brass. Carving: South German, c.1670–1680. Mount: probably Augsburg, from the same time.

1179　CUP: Rhinoceros horn. South German, c.1670–1680.

1180　TANKARD: Rhinoceros horn, silver-gilt. Carving: Franconian, c.1675. Mount: Johann Eissler, Nuremberg, c.1680–1690.

Raised relief on the sides: Negro on horseback and negro on foot in combat. Knop: Two negroes in combat.

1181–1191　ELEVEN BEAKERS: Ibex horn. Salzburg, c.1740–1750.

On one beaker is a relief of the Parish Church of Mülln (Salzburg). Since the first half of the 16th century the Archbishops of Salzburg bred ibex, first in the upper Ziller valley, later in the Tennen mountains and in Hellbrunn park.

1192　CUP: Eland's claw.

1193　AMULET: Eland's claw, gold. First half of 18th century.

Hollow Glassware

Towards the end of the 17th century Johann Kunkel in Potsdam invented the purple-red artificial ruby glass, intended to match the coloured brilliance of the precious stone. Production of the artificial ruby glass spread rapidly through numerous ateliers, the most prominent of which were in Nuremberg, Thuringia and Bohemia.

1194　CUP AND COVER: Ruby glass, silver-gilt, garnets. Ascribed to Johann Kunkel, Potsdam, c.1680.

1195　CUP AND COVER: Ruby glass, silver-gilt. Glass cutting: probably Heinrich Schwanhardt, Nuremberg, c.1680. Mount: Severinus Conrad Weiss.

1196–1202　SEVEN TRIANGULAR BOTTLES: Ruby glass, silver, parcel-gilt, diamonds. Allegedly Freising, c.1690–1700. Mount: probably Augsburg.

From the estate of Empress Maria Amalia, consort of Elector Carl Albrecht of Bavaria (1742–1745 as Emperor Karl VII).

1203–1206　FOUR SMALL BOTTLES: Ruby glass, silver-gilt. German, towards 1700.

1207–1208　TWO SHAPED GOBLETS: Ruby glass. German, towards 1700.

◁ Cat. 1173 Ornate cup and cover of rhinoceros horn, South German, c.1660

1209–1212 FOUR DRINKING GLASSES: Ruby glass. German, towards 1700.

1213 CUP: Glass, silver. German, c.1700.

1214 BEAKER: Ruby glass. Probably Nuremberg, c.1700.

1215–1218 FOUR SMALL BOTTLES WITH SCREW TOPS: Glass, silver-gilt, onyx. Probably Nuremberg, c.1710.

1219–1220 TWO SMALL BOTTLES: Ruby glass, silver-gilt. German (Augsburg?), c.1725.

Column of Trajan

1221 COPY OF TRAJAN'S COLUMN: White marble, Swedish granite, lapis lazuli, silver-gilt, bronze-gilt. Luigi Valadier, Bartholomäus Hecher and Peter Ramoser, Rome, 1774–1780.

This column is a copy of a triumphal column in the Forum Trajanum in Rome which was erected by Apollodorus of Damascus in 113 AD. The copy was acquired by Elector Karl Theodor in 1783 during a stay in Rome. It was first exhibited in the Picture Gallery on the Court Garden.

ROOM X

WORKS OF EXOTIC HANDICRAFTED ART

Turkey and Persia

1222   SEAL RING: Carnelian. Turkish, 16th century.

1223   DAGGER AND SHEATH: Gold, Burmese rubies, diamonds. Turkish, second half of 16th century.

1224   HORSE'S BREASTPLATE : Nephrite, silver, parcel-gilt, peridots, turquoises, garnets, carnelian, glass. Turkish, c.1600.

1225   KNIFE AND SHEATH: Nephrite, gold, rubies, turquoises, fish-skin. Turkish, c.1600. Sheath: 17th century.

1226   DAGGER AND SHEATH: Gold, partly enamelled, rubies. Probably Turkestan or Bokhara, c.1600.

1227   DAGGER AND SHEATH: Gold, Burmese rubies, turquoises. Turkish, early 17th century.

1228   RING: Gold, carved carnelian. Turkish and Arabian, 1660.

1229   BELT BUCKLE: Gold, diamonds, rubies. Turkish, 17th century.

According to tradition Elector Max Emanuel of Bavaria (r. 1679–1726) is said to have personally taken the item from a Turkish pasha during the storming of Belgrade.

1230   KNIFE: Nephrite, gold, precious stones, steel. Turkish, 17th century.

1231   KNIFE AND SHEATH: Milky quartz, gold, rubies, emeralds, fish-skin. Turkish, 17th century.

1232   KNIFE AND SHEATH: Milky quartz, gold, rubies, fish-skin. Turkish, 17th century.

Cat. 1229 Belt buckle, Turkish, 17th century   ▷

Cat. 1237 Jewel casket, Persian, 16th century   ▷▷

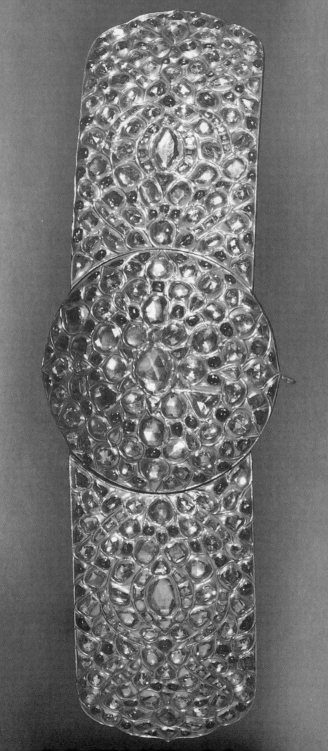

1233 KNIFE AND FORK WITH CASE : Silver, parcel-gilt, mother-of-pearl, fish-skin. Turkish, 17th century.

1234 RING: Chalcedony. Turkish, 17th century.

1235 KNIFE AND SHEATH: Bone, silver-gilt, mother-of-pearl, turquoises, corals. Turkish, early 18th century.

1236 KNIFE SHEATH: Fish-skin, enamelled gold. Turkish, 18th century.

1237 JEWEL CASKET: Wood, mother-of-pearl, ivory, gilded ironwork. Persian, 16th century. Reworked in Munich after 1635.

During reworking in Munich the marshalled coat-of-arms of the Bavarian Electorate and Austria were incorporated on the inside of the lid and gilded ironwork added to the outer corners, edges and feet.

1238 KNIFE: Chalcedony. Persian (late Ṣafavid dynasty), 17th century.

1239 RING: Gold, turquoises, ruby. Probably Persian, c.1600.

1240 TAPESTRY (known as the "Poland Tapestry"): Silk, gold threads. Persian, early 17th century.

From a tapestry collection which came into the possession of the Wittelsbach family through the marriage of the Polish Princess Anna Catharina with Elector Philipp Wilhelm von Pfalz-Neuburg (1642). Further "Poland tapestries" are to be found in the rear Electoral Chambers in the Munich Residence (East Asian collection).

Ceylon

1241 CHEST: Ivory, gold, rubies, sapphires. Ceylon (Sri Lanka), c.1545.

The figural reliefs show scenes from the time of the last Buddhist King of Ceylon who in 1542–1545 had sent a legation to the King of Portugal in Lisbon. Also depicted are Singhalese dancing scenes. The chest was acquired by Duke Albrecht V of Bavaria in Lisbon and since 1598 has been recorded in the inventory of the "Kunstkammer" (Collection of Cabinet Pieces) in Munich.

◁ Cat. 1241 Ivory chest, Ceylon, c.1545

1242 CHEST: Ivory, gold, enamel, rubies, emeralds, diamonds, pearls. Ceylon (Sri Lanka), c.1545. Mount: probably Munich, c.1570.

The figural reliefs show Portuguese hunting and jousting scenes. The chest was probably a gift to the Portuguese governor of Goa; it was probably brought over between 1542 and 1550 by a Singhalese delegation requesting help from Portugal for the Ceylonese King Bhuvaneka Bahu. As Cat. 1241 it was acquired in Lisbon by Duke Albrecht V of Bavaria and was first mentioned in Munich in 1598.

1243–1245 THREE COMBS: Ivory, gold, rubies. Ceylon (Sri Lanka), c.1540.

The combs were contained in the chest, Cat. 1242.

Eastern Asia

1246–1247 BOWL AND CREDENCE: Rhinoceros horn, gold, enamel, diamonds, rubies. Bowl: Chinese, late Ming period (Ming dynasty 1368–1643). Mount: South German, c.1570–1580. Credence: German, 17th century.

The shell with two dolphins, and Neptune and Amphitrite in the bowl were probably added in the early 18th century.

1248 BASIN: Porcelain, silver-gilt. Chinese porcelain: probably Tê-hua manufacture (Fujian province), from the time of the Ming Emperor Wan-li (1573–1619). Mount: Paris, c.1730.

1249 TANKARD: Porcelain, gold, silver-gilt, glass. Chinese porcelain: probably Tê-hua manufacture (Fujian province), from the time of the Ch'ing Emperor K'ang Hsi (1662–1722). Mount: Paris, 1729–1730. Porcelain lid and glass inset: probably French, from the same period.

1250–1251 REMAINS OF TWO FLACONS: Soapstone. Chinese, probably from the time of the Ch'ing Emperor K'ang Hsi (1662–1722).

1252–1253 BEAKER AND HOLDER: Soapstone, silver-gilt, textile, ornamental stones. Holder: Chinese, from the time of the Ch'ing Emperor K'ang Hsi (1662–1722). Beaker: David Winterstein, Augsburg, c.1680.

Cat. 1249 Chinese porcelain tankard. Mount: Paris, 1729–1730 ▷

1254   SMALL CUP AND COVER: Chalcedony, gold, onyx. Vessel: Chinese, from the time of the Ch'ing Emperor K'ang Hsi (1662–1722). Mount: French, c.1720.

1255   SAKE BOWL: Fired red clay. Chinese, Yi-hsing manufacture (Kiangsu province), from the time of the Ch'ing Emperor K'ang Hsi (1662–1722).

America

1256   SMALL BOWL: Basalt (?). South or Central American.

1257   RING: Gold. Mexico, Mixtecan, probably Monte Albán (Oaxaca), probably 15th century.

The ring was in the Ceylonese ivory chest Cat. 1242 and was acquired together with the chest by Duke Albrecht V of Bavaria. The ring was first mentioned in the inventory of the Munich Kunstkammer (Collection of Cabinet Pieces) in 1598 and is thus one of the earliest gold objects to arrive in Europe after the Spanish conquest of Mexico; the ring is therefore one of the few pieces from Monte Albán which escaped being melted down.

1258   HALF-LENGTH FIGURE WITH MEXICAN MINIATURE MASK: Pyroxenite, onyx, gold, partly enamelled, silver-gilt, bronze-gilt. Mask: Olmec, probably 500–1000 AD. Figure and niche: Guillaume de Groff (?), probably Munich, c.1720.

COLOUR PLATES
(Catalogue numbers placed in parantheses)

1 (11) Box with Hohenstaufen eagle cameo; cameo c. 1230, box c. 1720.

2 (4) Prayerbook of Charles the Bald, Rheims, 846 – 869, p. 38v.

3 (8) Cross of Queen Gisela , after 1006.

4 (13) Crown (known as "Henry's Crown"), c. 1280.

5 (16) Crown of an English Queen, c. 1370 – 1380.

6 (17) Pendant with Christ represented as the Man of Sorrows, towards 1400.

7 (19) Portrait medaillon, Burgundy, c. 1440.

8 (33) Salver, Valerio Belli, Venice or Padua, c. 1520.

9 (39) Chalice, Melchior Baier the Elder, Nuremberg, 1536.

10 (40) Bowl and cover, mount after designs by Hans Holbein the Younger, c. 1540.

11 (49) Double-headed eagle, c. 1550.

12 (57) Ornate chain, Munich, towards 1575.

13 (58) Statuette of St George, Munich and Augsburg, 1586 – 1597 and 1638 – 1641.

14 (61) Small private altar with scourging of Christ, ascribed to Ulrich Eberlin, Augusburg, c. 1575 – 1585.

15 (232) Franconian Duke's sword, c. 1455 – 1460 (detail).

16 (245) The King's crown of Bavaria, M.-G. Biennais, Paris, 1806 – 1807.

17 (246) The Queen's crown of Bavaria, Paris, 1806–1807, altered in 1867.

18 (459) Cup, heliotrope, Gasparo Miseroni, Milan, 1556.

19 (480) Ewer, Milan, c. 1570–1580.

20 (519) State table with pietra dura top, Prague and Augsburg, 1580/1626 (detail).

21 (567) Ornamental jug, Wenzel Jamnitzer, Nuremberg, c. 1570.

22 (579) Writing box, Hans and Elias Lencker, Nuremberg, c. 1580.

23 (565) Jewel casket, Wenzel Jamnitzer, Nuremberg, c. 1550–1560.

24 (562) "Sapphire Cup" Hans Reimer, Munich, 1563.

25 (561) Cup and cover, Hans Reimer, Munich, 1562.

26 (631) Brooch, Hans Georg Beuerl (jeweller), Augsburg, 1603.

27 (592) The Radziwil bowl, Nuremberg or Salzburg, after 1600.

28 (803) Hunting cup, J. J. Adam, Augsburg, 1753–1755.

29 (588) Diana with stag (drinking game), M. Walbaum, Augsburg, c. 1600.

30 (1091) Palatine Elector Johann Wilhelm as Mars, 1704.

31 (1099) Huntsman and dog, German, c. 1720.

32 (1258) Half-length figure with mexican miniature mask in niche, olmec, probably 500–1000 AD and Munich, c. 1720.

3

8

9

13

15

25

Bayerische Verwaltung der staatlichen Schlösser, Gärten und Seen

SEHENSWÜRDIGKEITEN

Ansbach	**Residenz der Markgrafen von Ansbach;** Prunkappartements des frühen Rokoko, Sammlung Ansbacher Fayencen und Porzellan, Hofgarten mit Orangerie	Tel. 0981/3186 Fax 0981/95840
Aschaffenburg	**Schloß Johannisburg** Gemäldegalerie und Kurfürstliche Wohnräume, Sammlung von Korkmodellen, Schloßgarten, Städtisches Schloßmuseum	Tel. 06021/22417 Fax 06021/218921
	Pompejanum; Nachbildung eines römischen Hauses und Antikenmuseum	
	Schloß und Park Schönbusch Klassizistisches Schlößchen in englischem Landschaftsgarten	
Bamberg	**Neue Residenz Bamberg** Kaisersaal und barocke Prunkräume, Gemäldegalerie, Rosengarten	Tel. 0951/56351 Fax 0951/55923
Bayreuth	**Neues Schloß** Markgrafenresidenz aus der Zeit des »Bayreuther Rokoko« mit Museum Bayreuther Fayencen, Hofgarten mit Orangerie	Tel. 0921/759690 Fax 0921/7596915
	Markgräfliches Opernhaus	

Bayreuth/ Donndorf	**Schloßpark Fantaisie** Historische Gartenanlage	Tel. 0921/759690 Fax 0921/7596915
Bayreuth/ Eremitage	**Altes Schloß Eremitage** Wohnräume der Markgräfin Wilhelmine, Grotte, historische Gartenanlage mit Wasserspielen	Tel. 0921/92561 Fax 0921/94540
Bayreuth/ Wonsees Sanspareil	**Morgenländischer Bau** Stilräume, Gartenparterre und Felsengarten **Burg Zwernitz,** Burganlage	Tel. 0921/759690 Fax 0921/7596915
Burghausen	**Burg zu Burghausen** Burganlage, Stilräume, Gemäldegalerie	Tel. 08677/4659 Fax 08677/65674
Coburg	**Schloß Ehrenburg** Historische Wohn- und Prunkräume des Barock und 19. Jahrhunderts	Tel. 09561/80880 Fax 09561/808840
Coburg/ Rödental	**Schloß Rosenau** in englischem Landschaftsgarten, Wohnräume der Biedermeierzeit und neugotischer Marmorsaal	Tel. 09563/4747 Fax 09561/808840
Dachau	**Schloß Dachau;** Festsaal, historische Gartenanlage	Tel. 08131/87923 Fax 08131/78573
Eichstätt	**Willibaldsburg** Festungsanlage, Juramuseum, Ur- und Frühgeschichtsmuseum, Hortus Eystettensis	Tel. 08421/4730 Fax 08421/8194
Ellingen	**Residenz Ellingen;** Prunk- appartements des Fürsten Wrede, Deutschordensräume, Schloßkir- che, historische Gartenanlage	Tel. 09141/3327 Fax 09141/72953

Herrenchiemsee	**Neues Schloß**	Tel. 08051/6887-0
	Herrenchiemsee	Fax 08051/6887-99
	Wohn- und Repräsentationsräu-	
	me, historische Gartenanlage mit	
	Wasserspielen und	
	König Ludwig II. Museum	
	Museum im Alten Schloß	
	Dauerausstellung zur ehemaligen	
	Klosteranlage und zum Ver-	
	fassungskonvent; Stilräume	
	König Ludwigs II.	
Hochstädt	**Schloß Hochstädt**	Tel. 08431/8897
	Kapelle mit Sammlung	Fax 08431/42689
	südwestdeutscher Fayencen	
Kelheim	**Befreiungshalle**	Tel./Fax 09441/1584
Kempten	**Residenz Kempten**	Tel. 0831/256-1
	Prunkräume und Thronsaal der	und 0831/256-251
	Fürstäbte	Fax 0831/256-260
Königssee	**St. Bartholomä;** Jagdschloß,	Tel. 08652/96360
	Kapelle St. Johann und Paul,	Fax 08652/64721
	Naturpark Berchtesgaden	
Kulmbach	**Plassenburg;** Schöner Hof,	
	historische Markgrafenzimmer,	Tel. 09221/4116
	Gemäldegalerie,	
	Jagdwaffensammlung	
Landshut	**Stadtresidenz;** Stilräume und	Tel. 0871/924110
	Gemäldegalerie, Kreis- und	und 0871/9241144
	Stadtmuseum	Fax 0871/9241140
	Burg Trausnitz	
	Burganlage mit Burgkapelle	
	St. Georg, Stilräume	

| Lauenstein bei Ludwigsstadt | **Burg Lauenstein** Burganlage, Wohnräume, volkskundliche Sammlungen | Tel. 09263/400 |

| Linderhof | **Schloß Linderhof** Wohn- und Repräsentationsräume, Venusgrotte, Marokkanisches Haus, Maurischer Kiosk und Hundinghütte, historische Gartenanlage mit Wasserspielen | Tel. 08822/3512 Fax 08822/3587 |

| München | **Residenzmuseum** Historische Wohn- und Prunkräume aus der Zeit der Renaissance bis zum 19. Jahrhundert, Hofkirchen und -kapellen, Spezialsammlungen (Silber, Porzellan, Paramente, Reliquien) | Tel. 089/290671 Fax 089/29067225 |

Schatzkammer

Altes Residenztheater
(Cuvilliés-Theater)

Hofgarten

Bavaria mit Ruhmeshalle
auf der Theresienhöhe

Tel. 089/508725

Schloß Nymphenburg
Prunk- und Stilräume,
Festsaal, Schönheitengalerie,
Schloßkapelle

Tel. 089/179080
Fax 089/17908627

Amalienburg, Badenburg, Pagodenburg, Magdalenenklause
im historischen Schloßpark

Marstallmuseum
Höfische Kutschen und Schlitten,
Reit- und Sattelzeug

Museum Nymphenburger Porzellan
Sammlung Bäuml

	Englischer Garten	Tel. 089/341986
	Landschaftsgarten im englischen Stil	Fax 089/335169
München/ Oberschleißheim	**Neues Schloß Schleißheim** Festsäle, Staatsappartements, Gemäldegalerie, barocker Hofgarten	Tel. 089/3158720 Fax 089/31587250
	Schloß Lustheim Porzellansammlung	
Neuburg a.d. Donau	**Schloßmuseum Neuburg a.d. Donau** Sgraffitofassade, Kapelle, Grotten; Vorgeschichte Pfalz-Neuburg, Kirchlicher Barock	Tel. 08431/8897 Fax 08431/42689
Neuschwanstein/ Schwangau	**Schloß Neuschwanstein** Wohn- und Repräsentations- räume	Tel. 08362/81035 und 08362/81801 Fax 08362/8990
Nürnberg	**Kaiserburg Nürnberg** Palas, Stilräume, Doppelkapelle, Tiefer Brunnen und Sinwellturm, Burggarten	Tel. 0911/225726 Fax 0911/2059117
Prunn im Altmühltal	**Burg Prunn** Stilräume	Tel. 09442/3323 Fax 09442/3335
Riedenburg	**Burg Rosenburg** Burganlage mit Kapelle; privat betriebener Falkenhof	Tel. 09442/2752 Fax 09442/3287
Schachen	**Königshaus am Schachen** Wohnräume und Maurischer Saal	Tel. 08821/2996

Schnaittach	**Festung Rothenberg** Ruine einer Festungsanlage aus dem 18. Jahrhundert	Tel. 09153/7793
Übersee/Feldwies	**Künstlerhaus Exter** mit Atelier des Malers Julius Exter	Tel. 08642/895083 Fax 08642/895085
Utting am Ammersee	**Künstlerhaus Gasteiger** Sommervilla mit Wohnräumen und Werken von Anna und Mathias Gasteiger, Villengarten	Tel. 08806/2682 und 08806/2091
Veitshöchheim	**Schloß und Park Veitshöchheim;** Historische Wohnräume, Rokokogarten mit Wasserspielen	Tel. 0931/91582 Fax 0931/51925
Würzburg	**Residenz Würzburg;** Barocke Prunkräume, Fresken von G.B. Tiepolo, Gemäldegalerie, Hofgarten	Tel. 0931/355170 Fax 0931/51925
	Festung Marienberg Festungsanlage, Fürstenbaumuseum mit Schatzkammer, Paramentensaal und stadtgeschichtliche Sammlungen, Maschikuliturm; Mainfränkisches Museum, Fürstengarten	

VERÖFFENTLICHUNGEN DER BAYERISCHEN VERWALTUNG DER STAATLICHEN SCHLÖSSER, GÄRTEN UND SEEN

Amtliche Führer   **je DM 4,00 – 6,00**
Deutsche Ausgaben:

Ansbach	Residenz Ansbach
Aschaffenburg	Schloß Aschaffenburg
	Pompejanum in Aschaffenburg
	Schloß und Park Schönbusch
Bamberg	Neue Residenz Bamberg
Bayreuth	Eremitage zu Bayreuth
	Markgräfliches Opernhaus Bayreuth
	Neues Schloß Bayreuth
Bayreuth/Wonsees	Felsengarten Sanspareil – Burg Zwernitz
Burghausen	Burg zu Burghausen
Coburg	Coburg – Schloß Ehrenburg
Coburg/Rödental	Schloß Rosenau
Dachau	Schloß Dachau
Eichstätt	Willibaldsburg Eichstätt
Ellingen	Residenz Ellingen
Herrenchiemsee	Neues Schloß Herrenchiemsee
Kelheim	Befreiungshalle Kelheim
Königssee	St. Bartholomä am Königssee
Kulmbach	Plassenburg ob Kulmbach
Landshut	Landshut Burg Trausnitz
	Stadtresidenz Landshut
Lauenstein bei Ludwigsstadt	Burg Lauenstein
Linderhof	Schloß Linderhof
München	Residenz München
	Schatzkammer der Residenz München
	Altes Residenztheater in München
	(Cuvilliés-Theater)
	Englischer Garten München
	Ruhmeshalle mit Bavaria
	Nymphenburg, Schloß, Park und Burgen
	Marstallmuseum in Schloß Nymphenburg
Neuburg a. d. Donau	Schloßmuseum Neuburg an der Donau
Neuschwanstein/Schwangau	Schloß Neuschwanstein

Nürnberg	Kaiserburg Nürnberg
Oberschleißheim	Schloß Schleißheim, Neues Schloß und Garten
Prunn	Burg Prunn
Riedenburg	Burg Rosenburg in Riedenburg an der Altmühl
Schachen	Königshaus am Schachen
Veitshöchheim	Veitshöchheim
Würzburg	Festung Marienberg zu Würzburg Residenz Würzburg und Hofgarten

English Editions:

Aschaffenburg	Aschaffenburg Castle and Pompeiianum
Bayreuth	The Hermitage at Bayreuth Margravial Opera House Bayreuth
Coburg	Coburg Ehrenburg Palace
Herrenchiemsee	The New Palace of Herrenchiemsee
Linderhof	Linderhof Palace
München	Residence Munich The Treasury in the Munich Residence Nymphenburg, Palace, Park, Pavilions Marstallmuseum Schloß Nymphenburg in Munich
Neuschwanstein/Schwangau	Neuschwanstein Castle
Nürnberg	Imperial Castle Nuremberg
Schachen	The Royal House on the Schachen
Würzburg	The Würzburg Residence and Court Gardens

Editions with English Summary:

Bamberg	Neue Residenz Bamberg
Bayreuth/Wonsees	Felsengarten Sanspareil – Burg Zwernitz
Burghausen	Burg zu Burghausen
Coburg/Rödental	Schloß Rosenau
Königssee	St. Bartholomä am Königssee
München	Englischer Garten München
Oberschleißheim	Schloß Schleißheim

Editions Françaises:

Herrenchiemsee	Le Nouveau Château de Herrenchiemsee
Linderhof	Le Château de Linderhof
München	Le Trésor de la Résidence de Munich Nymphenburg, Le Château, le Parc et les Pavillons

Neuschwanstein/Schwangau	Le Château de Neuschwanstein
Nürnberg	Le Château Impérial de Nuremberg
Schachen	Le Châlet Royal de Schachen
Würzburg	Wurtzbourg, Le Palais des Princes
	Évêques et les Jardins

Editions avec résumé français:

Bayreuth/Wonsees	Felsengarten Sanspareil - Burg Zwernitz
München	Englischer Garten München

Edizioni Italiane:

Herrenchiemsee	Castello di Herrenchiemsee
Linderhof	Castello di Linderhof
München	Tesoro della Residenz München
	Nymphenburg, Il Castello, il Parco e i Castelli del Giardino
Neuschwanstein/Schwangau	Castello di Neuschwanstein
Würzburg	La Residenza di Würzburg e il Giardino di Corte

Japanische Ausgaben:

Herrenchiemsee	Schloß Herrenchiemsee
Linderhof	Schloß Linderhof
München	Nymphenburg
Neuschwanstein/Schwangau	Schloß Neuschwanstein
Würzburg	Residenz Würzburg und Hofgarten

PROSPEKTE UND ZEITSCHRIFTEN

Prospekt „Ansbacher Fayencen"	DM 1,00
Prospekt „Nymphenburger Porzellan-Sammlung Bäuml"	DM 1,50
Prospekt „Königshaus am Schachen"	DM 1,50
Prospekt „Residenz Kempten (dt., engl.)"	DM 2,00
Prospekt „Schloß Rosenau"	DM 2,00
Prospekt „Schloßpark Linderhof"	DM 2,00
Zeitschrift „Vernissage", Sonderheft „Das Bayreuth der Markgräfin Wilhelmine/Schlösserreisen Franken"	DM 8,00

MUSEUMSPÄDAGOGISCHE SCHRIFTEN

Schloß Nymphenburg entdecken (1994)	DM 6,00

BILDHEFTE DER BAYERISCHEN SCHLÖSSERVERWALTUNG

Heft 1: HEYM, SABINE: **Das Alte Residenztheater/ Cuvilliés-Theater in München (**dt., engl., frz., ital.); München 1995   DM 15,00

Heft 2: HEYM, SABINE: **Amadis und Oriane - Im Zauber- reich der barocken Oper.** Tapisserien im Neuen Schloß Bayreuth, München 1998   DM 9,00

REIHE „FORSCHUNGEN ZUR KUNST- UND KULTURGESCHICHTE"

Band I: SANGL, SIGRID: **Das Bamberger Hofschreiner- handwerk im 18. Jahrhundert;** München 1990 (kartoniert)   DM 30,00

Band II: HOJER, GERHARD: **Die Prunkappartements Ludwigs I. im Königsbau der Münchner Residenz;** München 1992 (kartoniert)   DM 35,00

Band III: STIERHOF, HORST H.: **„das biblisch gemäl".** Die Kapelle im Ottheinrichsbau des Schlosses Neuburg an der Donau; München 1993 (broschiert)   DM 12,00

Band IV: STÖRKEL, ARNO: **Christian Friedrich Carl Alexander.** Der letzte Markgraf von Ansbach- Bayreuth; Ansbach 1995 (kartoniert)   DM 30,00

STÖRKEL, ARNO: **Christian Friedrich Carl Alexander.** Der letzte Markgraf von Ansbach- Bayreuth, 2. Auflage, im Bildteil ergänzt und erweitert; Ansbach 1998 (kartoniert)   DM 38,00

Band V: HOJER, GERHARD (Hrsg.): **Bayerische Schlösser - Bewahren und Erforschen;** München 1996 (kartoniert)   DM 85,00

Band VI: TOUSSAINT, INGO: **Lustgärten um Bayreuth.** Eremitage, Sanspareil und Fantaisie in Beschreibungen aus dem 18. und 19. Jahrhundert; Georg Olms Verlag, Hildesheim 1998 (kartoniert)   DM 68,00

REIHE „BAUDOKOMENTATIONEN"

o. Nr.: LAND-UND UNIVERSITÄTSBAUAMT AUGSBURG IM AUFTRAG DER BAYER. VERWALTUNG DER STAATLICHEN SCHLÖSSER, GÄRTEN UND SEEN (Hrsg.): Restaurierung Schloß Höchstädt, Festschrift zur Fertig- stellung des I. Bauabschnitts und zur Eröffnung der Fayencenausstellung am 19. Oktober 1995 (broschiert)   DM 6,00

o. Nr.:   LANDBAUAMT ROSENHEIM IM AUFTRAG DER
          BAYERISCHEN VERWALTUNG DER STAATLICHEN
          SCHLÖSSER, GÄRTEN UND SEEN (Hrsg.):
          Wasserspiele Herrenchiemsee, Festschrift 1994 (broschiert)   DM 15,00

Heft 1:   STAATLICHES HOCHBAUAMT WEILHEIM IM
          AUFTRAG DER BAYERISCHEN VERWALTUNG DER
          STAATLICHEN SCHLÖSSER, GÄRTEN UND SEEN (Hrsg.):
          Das Marokkanische Haus im Schloßpark Linderhof.
          - Band I; Bildheft (broschiert)   *ca. DM 12,00*
            Erscheinungstermin: Oktober 1998
          - Band II; Dokumentation zur Wiedererrichtung
            und Restaurierung (broschiert)   DM 20,00

AUSSTELLUNGSKATALOGE UND -BROSCHÜREN

BAYERISCHE VERWALTUNG DER STAATLICHEN
SCHLÖSSER, GÄRTEN UND SEEN (Hrsg.): **200 Jahre
Englischer Garten München 1789-1989;** München 1989
(broschiert)   DM 4,00

BAYERISCHE VERWALTUNG DER STAATLICHEN
SCHLÖSSER, GÄRTEN UND SEEN (Hrsg.): **Hortus
Eystettensis - ein vergessener Garten?;** München 1998
(broschiert)   DM 8,00

KRÜCKMANN, PETER O. (Bearb.): **Carlo Carlone
1686-1775.** Der Ansbacher Auftrag (kartoniert);
Arcos/Landshut 1990   DM 37,00
(Buchhandelspreis: DM 79,00)

KRÜCKMANN, PETER O. (Hrsg.): **Der Himmel auf
Erden - Tiepolo in Würzburg.** Band I Ausstellungs-   Bd. I: DM 39,00
katalog. Band II Aufsätze: Prestel, München/   Bd. II: vergriffen
New York 1996 (broschiert)
*(Buchhandelspreise/Leinen: Band I DM 78,00;
Band II DM 86,00; Band I+II DM 148,00)*

KRÜCKMANN, PETER O.: **Heaven on Earth -
TIEPOLO - Masterpieces of the Würzburg Years;**
Prestel, München/New York 1996 (broschiert)   DM 78,00

KRÜCKMANN, PETER O.: **Paradies des Rokoko,**
Band I Das Bayreuth der Markgräfin Wilhelmine
Band II Galli Bibiena und der Musenhof der
Wilhelmine von Bayreuth/Ausstellungskatalog;
Prestel, München/New York 1998 (broschiert)
*(Buchhandelspreise/Leinen: Band I DM 78,00;
Band II DM 86,00; Band I+II DM 148,00)*

Bd. I: DM 39,00
Bd. II: DM 65,00
Bd. I+II: DM 92,00

SCHMID, ELMAR D. und SABINE HEYM (Bearb.):
Josef Effner 1687–1745. Bauten für Kurfürst Max
Emanuel; München 1987 (broschiert)

DM 2,00

SCHMID; ELMAR D. (Bearb.): **Friedrich Wilhelm
Pfeiffer 1822–1891.** Maler der Reitpferde König
Ludwigs II.; Bayerland, Dachau 1988 (kartoniert)

DM 48,00

SCHMID, ELMAR D. und SABINE HEYM (Bearb.):
Mathias und Anna Gasteiger. Aus einem Münchner
Künstlerleben um 1900; Bayerland, Dachau 1985 (broschiert)

DM 15,00

SCHMID, ELMAR D.: **Der Krönungswagen Kaiser
Karls VII.** Wahl und Krönung in Frankfurt am Main 1742;
Bayerland, Dachau 1992 (broschiert)

DM 25,00

SCHMID, ELMAR D.: **Julius Exter** – Unbekannte Werke
aus dem Nachlaß seiner Schülerin Olga Fritz-Zetter;
München 1996 (broschiert)

DM 10,00

SCHMID, ELMAR D.: **Julius Exter** – Aufbruch in die
Moderne; Klinkhardt & Biermann, München/Berlin 1998
(broschiert)
(Buchhandelspreis/Leinen: DM 98,00)

DM 48,00

STIERHOF, HORST H.: **„das biblisch gemäl".** 450 Jahre
Schloßkapelle Neuburg an der Donau; München 1993
(broschiert)

DM 5,00

BESTANDSKATALOGE

FROSIEN-LEINZ, HEIKE und ELLEN WESKI (Bearb.):
Das Antiquarium der Münchner Residenz, Katalog der
Skulpturen. 2 Bände; Hirmer, München 1987 (Leinen)
– nur im Buchhandel erhältlich –

HELMBERGER, WERNER und VALENTIN KOCKEL
(Bearb.): **Rom über die Alpen tragen.** Fürsten sammeln
antike Architektur. Die Aschaffenburger Korkmodelle;
Arcos, Landshut 1993 (kartoniert) DM 35,00
(Buchhandelspreis: DM 59,50)

HOJER, GERHARD (Hrsg.): **König Ludwig II.-Museum
Herrenchiemsee, Katalog;** Hirmer, München 1986
(kartoniert) DM 35,00
(Buchhandelspreis: DM 48,00)

LANGER, BRIGITTE: **Die Möbel der Residenz München,
Band 1.** Die französischen Möbel des 18. Jahrhunderts, hrsg.
von Gerhard Hojer und Hans Ottomeyer; Prestel, München/
New York 1995 (broschiert) DM 98,00
(Buchhandelspreis/Leinen: DM 228,00) ab 1.12.1998: DM 118,00!

LANGER, BRIGITTE und ALEXANDER HERZOG VON
WÜRTTEMBERG: **Die Möbel der Residenz München,
Band 2.** Die deutschen Möbel des 16. bis 18. Jahrhunderts,
hrsg. von Gerhard Hojer und Hans Ottomeyer; Prestel,
München/New York 1996 (broschiert) DM 98,00
(Buchhandelspreis/Leinen: DM 228,00) ab 1.12.1998: DM 118,00!

LANGER, BRIGITTE, HANS OTTOMEYER und
ALEXANDER HERZOG VON WÜRTTEMBERG:
Die Möbel der Residenz München, Band 3. Möbel
des Empire, Biedermeier und Spätklassizismus, hrsg. von
Gerhard Hojer und Hans Ottomeyer; Prestel, München/
New York 1997 (broschiert) DM 98,00
(Buchhandelspreis/Leinen: DM 228,00) ab 1.12.1998: DM 118,00!

MILLER, ALBRECHT (Bearb.): **Bayreuther Fayencen;**
Arcos, Landshut 1994 (kartoniert) DM 28,00
(Buchhandelspreis: DM 49,80)

SEELIG, LORENZ: **Kirchliche Schätze aus bayerischen
Schlössern.** Liturgische Gewände und Geräte des 16. bis
19. Jahrhunderts; Deutscher Kunstverlag, Berlin 1984 (broschiert) DM 10,00

ZIFFER, ALFRED: **Nymphenburger Porzellan.**
Die Sammlung Bäuml/Bäuml Collection;
Arnoldsche, Stuttgart 1996 (broschiert) DM 98,00
(Buchhandelspreis/Leinen: DM 148,00)

WEITERE VERÖFFENTLICHUNGEN

BAYERISCHE VERWALTUNG DER STAATLICHEN
SCHLÖSSER, GÄRTEN UND SEEN (Hrsg.): **Vierte
Festschrift zum Wiederaufbau der Residenz München;
München 1959** (broschiert) DM 5,00

BAYERISCHE VERWALTUNG DER STAATLICHEN
SCHLÖSSER, GÄRTEN UND SEEN (Hrsg.): **Journal der
Bayerischen Verwaltung der staatlichen Schlösser
Gärten und Seen;** München 1995 (broschiert) DM 10,00

ERMISCHER, GERHARD: **Schloßarchäologie - Funde zu
Schloß Johannisburg in Aschaffenburg;** Museen der
Stadt Aschaffenburg/Bayerische Schlösserverwaltung,
Aschaffenburg 1996 (kartoniert) DM 48,00

FOCHT, JOSEF: **Die musische Aura der Markgräfin
Wilhelmine.** Musikinszenierung in der Kunst des
Bayreuther Rokoko; Peda, Passau 1998 (broschiert) DM 17,80

FOCHT, JOSEF und GURSKI, HANS: **Das Gloria der
Engel im Fürststift Kempten.** Musikdarstellungen in der
Basilika St. Lorenz und der Residenz; Peda, Passau 1998
(broschiert) DM 17,80

HEYM, SABINE: **Feenreich und Ritterwelt - die
Rosenau als Ort romantisch-literarischen Welterlebens.**
Sonderdruck aus „Bayerische Schlösser - Bewahren und
Erforschen"; München 1996 (broschiert) DM 4,00

HOJER, GERHARD (Hrsg.): **Der Italienische Bau.**
Materialien und Untersuchungen zur Stadtresidenz Landshut;
Arcos, Landshut 1994 (kartoniert) DM 38,00

HOJER, GERHARD und PETER O. KRÜCKMANN:
**Neues Schloß Bayreuth, Anton Raphael Mengs:
„Königin Semiramis erhält die Nachricht vom
Aufstand in Babylon"** (PATRIMONIA 49);
Kulturstiftung der Länder und Bayerische Schlösserver-
waltung, Berlin/München 1995 (broschiert) DM 20,00

KUNZ-OTT, HANNELORE und ANDREA KLUGE
(Hrsg.): **150 Jahre Feldherrnhalle.** Lebensraum einer
Großstadt; Buchendorfer, München 1994 (broschiert) DM 25,00

KUTSCHBACH, DORIS: **Tiepolo - Eine Reise um die Welt**
(aus der Kinderbuch-Reihe „Abenteuer Kunst"); Prestel,
München/New York 1996 (kartoniert) DM 22,80

LANGER, BRIGITTE: **Residenz München, zwei Kommoden des Bernard II Vanrisamburgh** (PATRIMONIA 134); Kulturstiftung der Länder und Bayerische Schlösserverwaltung, Berlin/München 1997 (broschiert)   DM 20,00

MISSLBECK-WOESLER, MARIA: **Die Flora des Englischen Gartens, München 1986** (kartoniert)   DM 15,00

NADLER; STEFAN (Bearb.): **Julius Exter.** Ein Chiemseemaler in Feldwies; München 1990 (broschiert)   DM 70,00

NICKL, PETER: **Parkett.** Historische Holzfußböden und zeitgenössische Parkettkultur; Klinkhardt & Biermann, München/Berlin 1995 (Leinen)   DM 78,00

SCHMIDT, ELMAR D.: **Das Exter-Haus** - Ein Künstlersitz am Chiemsee in Übersee-Feldwies; München 1997 (broschiert)   DM 10,00

SCHUSTER, RAINER: **Nymphenburger Porzellan.** Kostbarkeiten aus der Sammlung Bäuml und dem Residenzmuseum München; München 1997 (broschiert)   DM 8,00

SCHUSTER, RAINER: **Nymphenburg Porcelain.** Treasures from the Bäuml Collection and the Residence Museum Munich; München 1997 (broschiert)   DM 8,00

STIERHOF, HORST H. (Bearb.): **Das Walhnhaus.** Der italienische Bau der Stadtresidenz Landshut; Landshut 1994 (broschiert)   DM 16,00

PLAKATE

groß (A 1):

Schlösserland Bayern	DM 7,00
König Ludwig II. (Portrait von Ferdinand Piloty, 1865)	DM 7,00
Nymphenburger Porzellan-Sammlung Bäuml	DM 7,00
Marstallmuseum	DM 7,00
Residenz München	DM 7,00
Schatzkammer der Residenz München	DM 7,00
Schloß Rosenau	DM 7,00
Schloß Ehrenburg Coburg	DM 7,00
Schloß und Park Schönbusch	DM 7,00
Bayreuther Fayencen (Sammlung Rummel)	DM 7,00
Landshut: Burg Trausnitz - Stadtresidenz	DM 7,00

Residenz Kempten	DM 7,00
Ausstellungsplakat „Schätze aus Porzellan"	DM 8,00
Ausstellungsplakat „Das vergessene Paradies -	
Das Bayreuth der Markgräfin Wilhelmine"	DM 7,00
„Rom über die Alpen tragen"	
(Korkmodelle in Schloß Johannisburg)	DM 5,00
Schloßmuseum Neuburg an der Donau	DM 5,00

klein (A 2/A 3)

Korkmodell „Pantheon" (Schloß Johannisburg)	DM 5,00
Pompejanum Aschaffenburg	DM 5,00
Neue Residenz Bamberg	DM 5,00
Plan „Schloßpark Nymphenburg"	DM 5,00
Ausstellungsplakat „das biblisch gemäl" (Schloßkapelle Neuburg)	DM 3,00
Ausstellungsplakat „von denen schönen Gärten" (Schloß Fantaisie)	DM 5,00
Ausstellungsplakat „ Hortus Eystettensis" (Willibaldsburg Eichstätt)	DM 5,00

CD-ROM

Ludwig II. - Ich, der König.
Leben, Schlösser, Musik, Dynastie, Zeitgeschichte — DM 79,00

Ludwig II - I, the king.
Life, Castles, Music, Dynasty, Contemporary History — DM 79,00

VIDEOS DES BAYERISCHEN RUNDFUNKS

- Nymphenburg, Schloß und Park (PAL/dt.; NTSC/engl.)	DM 39,95
- Die Kaiserburg in Nürnberg (PAL/dt.)	DM 39,95
- Die Königsschlösser (PAL/dt., PAL/engl.; NTSC/engl.)	DM 39,95

Das Video „Die Königsschlösser" gibt es in englischer
Sprache in zwei verschiedenen Systemen: im PAL-System
(z.B. für Großbritannien und Südafrika) und im
NTSC-System (z.B. für USA, Kanada und Japan).

Ausstellungsvideos:

- Tiepolo in der Würzburger Residenz „Der Himmel auf Erden"	DM 39,95
- „Das vergessene Paradies" - Galli Bibiena und der Musenhof der Wilhelmine von Bayreuth	DM 29,95

Preise zzgl. Porto und Verpackung, Bestellungen bitte an:
Bayerische Schlösserverwaltung, Postfach 38 01 20, 80614 München